Reader's Digest Paperbacks

Informative.....Entertaining.....Essential.....

Berkley, one of America's leading paperback publishers, is proud to present this special series of the best-loved articles, stories and features from America's most trusted magazine. Each is a one-volume library on a popular and important subject. And each is selected, edited and endorsed by the Editors of Reader's Digest themselves!

Berkley/Reader's Digest books

THE EDITORS OF *READER'S DIGEST*

REAL LIFE MYSTERIES

A BERKLEY/READER'S DIGEST BOOK
published by
BERKLEY BOOKS, NEW YORK

REAL LIFE MYSTERIES

A Berkley/Reader's Digest Book, published by arrangement with
Reader's Digest Press

PRINTING HISTORY
Berkley/Reader's Digest edition/August 1982

ISBN: 0-425-05608-2

Grateful acknowledgment is made to the following organizations and individuals for permission to reprint material from the indicated sources:

The Harold Matson Company, Inc. for "A Strange Tale of the South Seas" by James Ramsey Ullman, copyright © 1960 by the Curtis Publishing Co. Mr. Carl Bakal for "Linda's Haunting Vision" by Carl Bakal, copyright © 1972 by Carl Bakal. Mrs. Mabel Langdon Eiseley for "People Leave Skulls With Me" by Loren Eiseley, copyright © 1951 by Harper & Brothers. The Saturday Evening Post for "The Night My Number Came Up" by Air Marshal Sir Victor Goddard, copyright © 1951 by The Curtis Publishing Company. Mr. Jhan Robbins and Mrs. June Mellies Reno for "The Psychic Power of Sam Benson" by Jhan Robbins and June Mellies Reno, copyright © 1964 by United Newspapers Magazine Corp. Mr. Paul Deutschman for "It Happened on the Brooklyn Subway" by Paul Deutschman, copyright © 1949 by The Reader's Digest Association. "The Strange Story of Hector, The Stowaway Dog" by Captain Kenneth Dodson, reprinted by permission from The Christian Science Monitor, copyright © 1956 by The Christian Science Publishing Society. All rights reserved. Popular Science Monthly for "Runaway Engine on the Main Line" by E.D. Fales Jr., copyright © 1961 by Popular Science Publishing Company, Inc. American Legion Magazine for "Close Encounter of Flight 101" by Larry Engelmann, copyright © 1981 by the American Legion Magazine. T. Raines & Raines for "A Bullet From Nowhere" from the book CHIEF: CLASSIC CASES FROM THE FILES OF THE CHIEF OF DETECTIVES by Albert Seedman and Peter Hellman copyright © 1974 by Albert Seeman and Peter Hellman. "The Relic Men" from the book THE NIGHT COUNTRY by Loren Eiseley, copyright © 1971 by Charles Scribner's Sons, reprinted with permission. "The Most Dangerous Game" from the book THE MOST DANGEROUS GAME by Richard Connell, copyright © 1924 by Richard Connell, copyright renewed © 1952 by Louise Fox Connell, reprinted by permission of Brandt & Brandt Inc. Little, Brown & Co. and A.D. Peters & Co. Ltd. for "The Man Who Likes Dickens" from the book A HANDFUL OF DUST by Evelyn Waugh, copyright © 1934, 1962 by Evelyn Waugh. "Astral Projection and the Horse that Could Count" from BROCA'S BRAIN by Carl Sagan, copyright © 1974, 1975, 1976, 1977, 1978, 1979 by Carl Sagan. Reprinted by permission of Random House Inc.

Contents

Contents

Strange Stories,
Tantalizing Tales

It Happened
in the South Seas

by James Ramsey Ullman

THE WIND blew. Clouds hid the sun. The sea heaved. With the angry squalls and veils of driving rain, this was not the South Pacific of the travel books.

I was a passenger aboard the *Chicot,* a 3900-ton freighter serving the Trust Territory of the Pacific Islands—a huge area once held by Japan, now administered as a United Nations Trust Territory by the United States. Alone in a world of water, we were 11 days out of Guam, bound for Truk in the Eastern Carolines. I awoke in my cabin very early that morning, with the gray light of dawn coming through my porthole. The ship was slowing, stopping in the middle of nowhere.

In three minutes I was on deck. The sea was the heaviest I had yet seen, and as the *Chicot* lost speed it pitched and wallowed in the sullen swell. Capt. Edward A. O'Neill II, on the bridge, gestured to me to join him.

"Look there," he said, pointing.

I looked and saw nothing, until he gave me his binoculars and aimed me properly. Then I saw it: a canoe. I turned to him in disbelief. "It's no bigger than a log," I said.

"That's right—a hollow log with a mast. About a 20-footer, I'd say."

On a lake it would have looked small enough. On the vast Pacific it seemed not even a toy boat, but rather a chip of wood, a floating speck. From the decks of the *Chicot* we stared at it as if at an apparition from another world. Which, in a way, it was.

I saw that there were men aboard the canoe, moving about like ants on a blade of grass that has been washed away. But they had not made any signal. Were they in trouble?

"If they're not," said O'Neill, "there's no such thing as trouble."

The *Chicot* maneuvered so that wave and wind bore the small craft straight toward us. Like all Micronesian canoes, it was an outrigger: without the balance thus provided, it would have swamped in a twinkling. Amidships, lashed to its outrigger struts, was a platform supporting a low shelter of thatch and leaf. And above the shelter rose the sailless mast.

There were moments, as the waves climbed high, when the mast was all that was visible. Then the rest would bob up again, and we could see the craft's five occupants. Though they appeared haggard and weather-beaten, they were all functioning: one man steering, others bailing. One was elderly, one middle-aged, and three were scarcely more than boys. All were naked except for crimson loincloths.

In ten minutes they were alongside and the *Chicot* hove to, with engines still. The canoe looked tinier than ever under the high, black cliff of the *Chicot*'s hull.

Our chief mate, Stanley Gilje, was on the forward deck directly above the canoe. A colloquy began, with members of our crew acting as interpreters. Apparently the castaways weren't sure they *wanted* to be rescued. Where were we bound? they inquired. Truk, someone shouted. After more palaver, the mate reported: "Okay. They say they'll come aboard if the canoe comes, too."

"That's damn nice of them," said the captain. "All right. Haul it up."

Now winches ground and booms moved overhead. Two wire slings were lowered and passed under the canoe, and a rope was attached to the outrigger for balance. Four of the canoeists seized our rope ladder and came scrambling up. However, the oldest, the helmsman, elected to stay with his craft to the end. The winches clattered again, and the canoe was swung on deck.

The old helmsman sat in the stern, composed and motionless. From a string around his neck hung a glittering pendant that I took for an amulet but which later proved to be a GI can opener. On his lap he carefully guarded a rusted wreck of a compass.

As soon as the canoe was down, the four other rescuees rejoined the helmsman in it. We stood watching them like yokels at a county fair.

Their craft was, as estimated, about 20 feet long—not cut from a single log but made of planks of breadfruit wood, held together by strips of coral cement and thongs of coconut fiber, with not a single nail in the whole structure. The canoe proper was narrow and deep, a mere slot in which a man could squat or kneel. Its shelter, on the struts of the outrigger, was perhaps a yard square and 18 inches high. Two men at most—small and pretzel-limbed—could have fit into it at one time, for shelter or sleep.

The canoe's sail, a sodden mass of store-bought blue denim, was wedged under a thwart near the bow. There was no sign of food; only bits of charcoal, and a few battered pots and gourds which had seen a lot more service for bailing than for eating. Even now, on the *Chicot*, water was a foot deep in the canoe, and its proprietors were bailing away industriously. Out on the open sea it must have been like—"like being in a bathtub," the chief mate said, "with the faucets stuck open."

Through with bailing, the five men spread the sail out to dry, inspected the seams of the hull, tightened the fibrous bindings. Their concern was all for their craft. Implausibly, none of them seemed to need any medical care. That they needed food, however, was obvious. Persuaded that the canoe was all right, they finally consented to visit the galley. Odds and ends of clothing were produced to replace their soaked loincloths. They even proved human enough, with some urging, to rest for a while. Afterward we sat down with them— and a crewman interpreter—to hear their story.

The eldest of them, the helmsman, did all the talking. His name was Sernous, he said; the others were members of his family group, or clan. They came from the atoll of Pulap, and were going to Truk.

From Pulap—in the canoe? The captain opened a map. "But Pulap," he pointed out, "is 300 miles east. And Truk's 150 miles *beyond* Pulap. So you were lost, then?"

"No, we were blown away."

They had been at sea 30 days. Sernous opened his gnarled hands three times, showing all the fingers. "Thirty," he re-

peated. The trip should have taken four days—he had made
it often before. But this time there had been big winds, big
waves. And besides, his compass had gone wrong. It was an
old compass from a Japanese fishing boat, and it leaked alcohol
all over. Perhaps the captain could fix it.

Anyhow, the old man continued, they had been pushed back
to the west, day after day. The wind had been so strong that
they could do nothing against it. They had had to bail in shifts,
all day and all night. Even so, for much of the time, the *Santa
Maria* was half under water.

That was their canoe, the *Santa Maria*? They were Cath-
olics, then?

Yes. Sernous glanced down at his GI can opener as if it
were a crucifix, and crossed himself.

What about food? At the beginning, we were told, they had
coconuts, taro and breadfruit, with charcoal and flint to make
a fire. When this food was gone and the charcoal soaked, they
caught fish and ate them raw. They had been lucky with the
fishing. They had caught about 30, almost one a day. And they
had been lucky with water, too; they had collected enough rain
to drink. The nights were the hardest, for they were always
wet and cold.

Did they know where they had been when we found them?

Oh, yes. They had been hoping to reach the atoll of Ifalik,
in the district of Yap. "Is that way," Sernous said, pointing to
the northwest. And the captain and mate nodded in bemused
agreement. Ifalik was indeed "that way"; 35 miles, by the
ship's chart, from where we had sighted them, and almost 500
from their destination at Truk.

Later, we discussed what *we* would have been like, physically and emotionally, after 30 days in that chip of a boat in
mid-ocean; how *we* would have reacted to the experience of
rescue. As he told his story, the old helmsman of Pulap spoke
in a matter-of-fact monotone. His companions, too, showed
no strain or emotion. They had been lost at sea. So—thousands
of their people, over the centuries, had been lost; some had
been found and some had not; some, even in our own time,
had been borne as far as New Guinea and the Philippines.

Thirty days, 500 miles: what was that? Nothing. The answer
was in their relaxed bodies and their placid brown eyes.

Sernous was speaking again, and the interpreter said, "He
asks please can they go back now to work on their canoe. They

want it to be strong and not leak on the way from Truk back to Pulap."

"Sure," said Captain O'Neill. Then he thought of one further question. "Ask them why they were going to Truk in the first place."

Sernous spoke, and the interpreter said, "They were going to buy cigarettes."

"That's all? To buy cigarettes?"

"Yes. Cigarettes. He says there is nothing else they need."

We produced a carton apiece for them, and for the rest of the voyage our guests chain-smoked while they worked on the *Santa Maria*. What brand they had intended to buy they didn't tell us. But there were no complaints.

The Corpse at the Table

by Samuel Hopkins Adams

WHEN I first heard the story of the two blizzard-bound men on the mountain, I assumed that it was part of the folklore of the Adirondack region. Since then, I have questioned many people about it and, though many of them recall it, none is able to identify the origin. Therefore it may well be folklore on the imaginative rather than on the realistic side. But who wrote it, and where?

AN OCTOBER blizzard had caught two surveyors wholly unprepared in the heart of the Adirondacks. They were Charles Carney and Stephen Estelow, old working companions and close friends. Through gale and drift they floundered doggedly all day, Estelow, powerfully built and more youthful, giving aid to his slender mate who was spent in body and spirit.

Now, as light was failing, Estelow gave a cry of hope. Straight-drawn against the darkening whirl ran a feathery line.

"The wire! The telegraph wire."

"Yes; but where to?" coughed Carney. "And how far? I'm going to burrow in and sleep."

"No, you're not," Estelow commanded. "This must be the line the government survey strung last spring from their shack to railhead at North Creek. All we have to do now is climb. Come on!"

He urged and dragged his companion up through the woods

8

until, after a half hour of struggle, they reached the cabin. They were in luck. Wood was plentiful. Some ears of dried corn lay on the shelf. A stormbound porcupine whimpered in a treetop. Estelow shot it with his revolver. Starvation was a remote threat. But by now Carney was ill, burning with fever. After firing the stove to red heat, Estelow got him to bed in the inner room.

In the morning Carney seemed a little better. And the telegraph was a hope, for Carney could "send." Weak though he was after a night of pain, he staggered out to the table and opened the switch.

The operator at North Creek thought himself crazy when he received the call from Lonely Hill. The code was halting but intelligible. Two men marooned on the summit, one with pneumonia. Well, God help them! Man could not. Not yet. The blizzard raged with mounting fury. Twenty-four hours later another message chattered across the wire. Now it was wild with delirium. The cabin was under siege by hideous beasts, by white-winged angels, fiends whose fiery eyes glowed through the storm. The Morse shivered into incoherence.

Estelow had carried his frail companion back to bed. Again and again in semilucid intervals next morning Carney managed to crawl to the table and sit at the key, tapping out stuttering Morse. But North Creek no longer got the calls. The line had gone dead, borne down by snow and wind.

Toward evening, Estelow once more tucked his delirious companion into bed and went outdoors in search of firewood. He returned to find Carney seated before the transmitter. His face was composed.

"Steve," said the sick man quietly, "Steve, I think I'm dying. But, Steve," he pleaded with burning eyes, "don't bury me until you're sure I'm dead. It might be only a coma." He gasped. "Don't, Steve, don't bury me alive—" His voice trailed off in a whisper.

Estelow's grief-stricken voice and eyes gave a solemn promise.

What followed in the next days Estelow faithfully entered, item by item, in his diary. It was while he was making a stew that evening, with the last of the porcupine, that his sick friend rose, crept to his place at the table and there died. Testing for pulse and breath, Estelow made sure of death.

Rigor mortis gave the heartsick survivor convincing evidence for burial. With a fire spade he scooped a hole in a high drift, set the body in it, said a prayer, and shoveled in the snow. He passed a night of grisly dreams, waking once, chilled to the heart with what he took to be a cold sweat.

In the morning when he crawled out of bed and went to replenish the fire, Charles Carney was sitting at the table, motionless, speechless, staring.

All that day, his mind frozen in a stupor of horror and incredulity, Estelow left the corpse untouched while he tramped through the drifts outside, seeking food. At nightfall, summoning all his mental powers to keep a grip on reality, he returned Charles Carney's body to the insufficient grave. In his kit was a flask still half full of brandy. He drank it all and went to bed.

To force himself out in the morning demanded a mighty effort of will. For a full minute he stood, shivering and shaking, before he could open the door to the main room.

Charles Carney was seated there at the table as before.

"I shall try to keep my sanity to the last," Estelow wrote in his record. "If he comes back again, I shall know what to do." Again he tramped the woods all day, wildly reasoning with himself. He was probably suffering hallucinations. But he certainly wasn't crazy. Maybe it was all a vivid nightmare. He returned to the shack, flung open the door.

There Charles Carney still sat.

After the third burial that evening Estelow was afraid to go to bed. He sat across the table from the empty chair and fought against sleep. Exhaustion overcame him. His head fell forward.

Gray dawn awoke him. Blurred in the gloom, Charles Carney again sat opposite. The eyes stared at nothingness.

"God help me," Estelow wrote. It was the last entry.

THE RESCUE PARTY, two woodsmen, a physician, and Clark, the North Creek telegraph operator, thrust their snow-shoed feet wearily up the last slope to the cabin. It was without sign of life. No smoke rose from the chimney. Human foot-prints formed a deep trail from the door to a snowdrift curiously hollowed out. The doctor pushed open the door. The interior was silent and bitingly cold. At the table sat two dead men.

Both had been shot through the head. Estelow had slumped forward in a pool of blood, now congealed. The revolver lay on the floor beneath his lax right hand. Carney sat propped upright in his chair. His eyes were open, his expression calm.

"Murder and suicide!" exclaimed the telegrapher. "Poor devils!"

The doctor had been examining the bodies. "Not murder," he said. He touched Carney's forehead. "No blood here. The man was already dead when shot. And, I think, frozen."

The five rescuers exchanged looks of utter mystification. One of the woodsmen picked up Estelow's diary and handed it to the doctor. He mused over it, then went outside to study the prints in the snow. When he returned he lit his pipe, smoked thoughtfully, and finally spoke.

"Friends, for the sake of the families of the dead, I bind you all to secrecy. I am a coroner. It is my official verdict that Charles Carney and Stephen Estelow came to their death by cold, hunger and privation. Is that understood?"

One after another the men nodded their agreement. It was the North Creek telegrapher who spoke haltingly, in a hushed tone of bewilderment.

"I'd sleep easier—if I could know—what happened."

"And I," said the doctor. "The best I can do is a guess. If we find that Estelow was a sleepwalker, I shall be sure. This is what happened, as I see it. At night in his sleep, Estelow dug out the body from where he had buried it and put it back in the chair where he had last seen his friend alive. Why? The desperate nervous horror of his loneliness, perhaps. And a subconscious effort to comply with his solemn assurance to Carney that he would be absolutely certain of death. That, at least, would explain the shooting. At any rate, the exhumation was repeated once and again.

"Some subtle instinct must have tried to warn Estelow, after the second return, that he must not lose his hold on consciousness, but nature was too strong for him. Again he slept and the demon of somnambulism took charge of his actions. At the last his spirit gave way under the strain."

Estelow's record was destroyed and the two bodies consigned to the depths of a mountain lake.

Linda's Haunting Vision

by Carl Bakal

LIFE BEGAN for Linda Buritsch on September 10, 1945, on Staten Island, N.Y. When she was two, the Buritsch family, which also included Linda's older brother, Kit, moved to Riviera Beach, Md. Although Linda was born with a heart murmur, she lived a completely active life—swimming, fishing, playing tennis. When she was a child, she dreamed of becoming a gym teacher, but as she grew older her interests turned to music, art and writing.

She wrote poetry and stories, some of which were published in student anthologies. Death seemed to preoccupy her. "What is death?" she once wrote. "Death is eternity—but how can I be sure?" Was it her awareness of death that made life so precious to her? "I love life," she wrote. "I wait for life. Will life wait for me?" She was always falling in and out of love. Although some of her attachments were serious, none was lasting, perhaps because the love she ultimately hoped to find existed only in her dreams.

This is suggested by a rather curious incident. One afternoon in 1963, just after she finished high school, she suddenly sketched a portrait—the first she had ever done. It was of a boy of about her own age who bore no resemblance to anyone she had ever known.

"Who's the boy?" her mother, Polly, asked.

"My dream man," said Linda.

"Oh, come off it," Polly said. "Where did you get such an idea?"

"I don't know," said Linda. "I just had an impulse to draw somebody, and that's who I came up with." Then she walked into her bedroom, removed a photograph from a frame, and replaced it with the portrait.

Linda attended Hood College in Frederick, Md., where she majored in English, continued her writing, and edited the school literary magazine. Upon graduation in 1967, she taught English at Annapolis Junior High School, and became one of the most popular teachers.

She had begun getting headaches while she was in college. But because they usually occurred at exam time, they were diagnosed as migraines triggered by pressure. Neither Linda nor her parents were alarmed.

In the spring of what was to be the last year of her life, she went on vacation to Puerto Rico and took several weekend trips to New England with friends. She was sparkling at her brother Kit's wedding in May and, after school was out in June, she dated almost every night.

"It now seems she sensed her time was running out," her mother recalls. "She kept going constantly." At one point she surprised everyone by thoroughly cleaning her room, throwing away old love letters and other mementos. But she saved the portrait of her "dream man," removing it from the frame and carefully placing it in a portfolio with her other sketches.

She was still troubled by occasional headaches, but the attacks did not seem to incapacitate her. Or it may be that Linda was simply not one to complain. Otherwise, she seemed in perfect health.

The end came with terrible suddenness. On Sunday, July 21, Linda came home from a weekend trip complaining of an unusually bad headache. Despite continuing pain, she worked at her temporary summer job most of the week, but on Thursday night she became violently ill, and threw up. "She may be allergic to codeine," the doctor told Polly over the phone, and prescribed another pain-killer. It enabled Linda to sleep through the night. But Friday morning Linda was far too sick to go to work. And during the day she started throwing up what appeared to be blood. Seriously alarmed, her mother phoned the doctor, who told her to take Linda to nearby North Arundel

Hospital. "Oh, Mom," Linda cried on the way, "I feel terrible. I think I'm going to die."

AT ALMOST THE SAME TIME, 400 miles away in Charleston, S.C., another 22-year-old faced tragedy of a different sort. If Linda might be described as the All-American girl, George (Woody) Johnson, Jr., was in many ways the All-American boy. Like Linda, in his growing-up years he had wanted to be a gym teacher and then—again like Linda—he found his interests turning to reading, drawing and music.

But Woody was always plagued with poor eyesight, and when he was 20 he learned that he was suffering from keratoconus, a rare disorder that may markedly distort vision and is characterized by a bulging of the membrane covering the front of the eye. At first, contact lenses flattened out the bulge in the left cornea and enabled him to see normally. Later, as the disease progressed, the lenses no longer did the job. By the spring of 1968, the ailment had progressed so far that Dr. William Vallotton, a prominent Charleston eye surgeon, told the boy a corneal transplant was needed to save the eye.

Woody agreed to the operation. Now the problem was to obtain an eye from a donor with little delay. Dr. Vallotton, who had performed several hundred such transplants, filed his request with the South Carolina Eye Bank, which in turn contacted the nation's other eye banks.

When Woody got home from college at the end of June, he was told to leave word where he could be reached at all times (corneal transplants must be performed within 72 hours of the removal of the eye from the donor). All that remained was for someone to die.

WHEN SHE ARRIVED at North Arundel Hospital, Linda was barely conscious. That evening a diagnostic spinal tap indicated some pressure on the brain, a condition the hospital wasn't equipped to handle. Linda, now in a coma, was sped by ambulance 15 miles to University Hospital in Baltimore. There she was rushed into surgery. Not until 1 A.M. Friday night— nearly five hours later—was Linda brought into the recovery room.

The surgeon was grim and gray with fatigue. "Your daughter had a brain tumor," he told Linda's parents. He added that he had done everything he could, that what happened now was up to God.

Linda never regained consciousness. At 1:45 A.M. Monday morning, the phone rang in the Buritsches' bedroom. "I knew immediately what it was," recalls Polly—"the hospital telling us it was over."

In the dazed confusion that followed, she recalls only hazily being asked if Linda's eyes could be donated to the eye bank. "I agreed," she says. "I felt Linda would have wanted me to. I remember once when we were discussing heart transplants, she said, 'I wish I could give my heart.' She knew that she couldn't, because her heart wasn't that good. But she said, 'I'd really like to leave something. It would be great to leave something.'"

Shortly after Linda's death, her eyes were delivered to the Medical Eye Bank of Maryland. At the top of the bank's list was the request of Woody's doctor in Charleston. Within minutes, Woody, who was working as a lifeguard at a Charleston swimming pool, got a message to phone his doctor. "We've got the eye," said Dr. Vallotton. "It's being flown in from Baltimore. I want you at the hospital by six this evening."

By 11 A.M. the next morning, the cornea of Woody's left eye had been replaced with one of Linda's.

DURING his weeks of convalescence, Woody's thoughts kept covering the same ground. How lucky he was to get a cornea so soon. Who was it who had given him the gift of sight? Was he ever going to be able to tell the donor's family how grateful he was?

Although he knew that the identity of eye donors is kept confidential (all he could learn from the hospital records was that his donor had been a 22-year-old), Woody wrote to the Medical Eye Bank of Maryland in late August 1968: "If, in your judgment, there would be no offense taken, I would like to say a humble 'thanks' to the family. If they would care to know, I am also 22 years of age, and I am a junior majoring in psychology at the University of Tennessee. The operation went very well and I'm recovering beautifully."

Frederick Griffith, director of the eye bank, had in the previous five years shipped perhaps 3000 corneas to all parts of the country. This was only the second time he had ever received a thank-you letter. Moved by Woody's sincerity, he phoned the Buritsches and read them the letter. Almost as an afterthought, he asked if they would like to meet Woody. They said yes.

On Saturday, October 6, Woody flew to Washington to be the Buritsches' guest for the weekend. He was nervous and apprehensive. After all, in his head was a piece of tissue that had once *lived* in the daughter of the people he was going to visit.

WOODY and the Buritsches hit it off instantly. "What surprised me," recalls a friend who was present at the meeting, "was that though these people had never met before, they felt comfortable and warm with each other. It was not at all like an encounter between strangers."

Polly Buritsch brought out Linda's portfolios and scrapbook and told Woody of Linda's many interests. He peppered the Buritsches with questions about Linda. That night—Polly had put Woody in Linda's room—Woody found her books as she had left them scarcely two months before: D. H. Lawrence, e. e. cummings, Emily Dickinson, Rilke, Shelley, Hemingway, Hegel—many of the books he also had read and loved.

At breakfast, Woody said he would have only black coffee. But after looking at Polly's pancakes, he changed his mind and filled his plate with a towering stack. How strange, thought Polly. Linda, too, would have done that—first refusing and then changing her mind. Polly noticed other similarities between this boy and her daughter. They had the same contagious laugh and bubbly way of expressing themselves. It was astonishing to think that anyone else—and particularly this boy—could be so like Linda. How uncanny it was that he should now be sitting in her place at the table.

Before leaving, Woody gave the Buritsches a photograph of himself, which Polly promptly had framed and placed on the living-room table. As the months passed, she would catch herself staring at it for no apparent reason. Why did she feel drawn to it? Was it because of the many similarities between Woody and Linda? Or because of the unique chain of events that had made Woody's life inextricably part of her own? But, no, it was something about the photograph itself. Where had she seen it before?

In the spring of 1969—six months after Woody's visit—

Left: Linda Buritsch's sketch of her "dream man," drawn in 1963 (five years before her death).

Right: A 1972 photograph of Woody Johnson, whom she never met.

the Buritsches decided to publish Linda's poetry and sketches as a memorial to her. Going through her things, Polly came across a sketch she hadn't seen for years—a portrait of a boy.

"My God, I can't believe it!" she cried out. She called her husband. "Who is this?" she asked, showing him the sketch. "Why, it's Woody," he said. Polly rushed to the living room and placed the portrait next to Woody's photo. The resemblance was astonishing. The portrait was the one Linda had made, five years before her death, of her dream man.

In the same portfolio, exactly where Polly had found the sketch, was a fragment of Linda's verse:

> *Of anguish, none is greater*
> *Than the passing of two hearts*
> *That never knew each other.*

In a Great Man's Shoes

by Walter B. Pitkin

THREE TIMES I've missed death by seconds; once I stared up through a foot of ice as rescuers chopped through. I've been on board a burning steamer; adrift on ice floes through a winter night. I've crouched behind a post while gangsters all around shot one another.

But such adventures seem minor when I contrast them with an afternoon I spent years ago with a little shoemaker in his smelly side-street shop.

He talked as he showed me his wares. I asked questions. Nothing else happened. Yet those few hours were the most extraordinary of my life. What happened could have happened only to me—and then only on a one-in-a-trillion chance.

You cannot understand that afternoon unless you know certain things about my past.

WHEN Woodrow Wilson became president of Princeton, he assembled some 50 young preceptors to start a new system of teaching there. He drew several from Columbia, and Columbia scouted for new men. They wanted a cheap youngster to teach psychology. I was cheap.

Columbia's faculty dragged me into golf and tennis. Wishing to be polite, I struggled away at the games. Years passed before I finished 18 holes of golf. Around the eighth or ninth hole my feet usually went on strike. Twinges climbed my legs.

I hurt all the way up to my neck. I grew so weak I couldn't swing a club.

I could play tennis for only half an hour at a stretch. Then one day along came a high, hot ball. I leaped. I swatted it. I returned to earth eventually. A hot coal started to burn underneath the foot—no, it was inside. I crumpled up in a shapeless heap.

"Broken transverse arch," said the university physician.

I used to study the effects of the broken arch during the two years it was healing. The linkage of burn to pain, of pain to weakness, and of weakness to ill temper was striking. After I'd been on my feet too long or fatigued myself, I felt a burning sensation under the middle toe. Soon it became a sharp, needle-like pain. Then I'd suddenly go weak all over. Some minutes later the ill temper would start. It was as uncontrollable as a sneeze. I'd shun people. When I had to talk, I'd grunt the fewest possible surly remarks.

I found little in medical libraries on the psychological effects of foot troubles. I queried outstanding medical authorities. "The effects are determined largely by the personality of the patient," they told me. "And nobody has yet analyzed that well enough. People react emotionally to a disease in a manner determined by their total nature." That persuaded me to tackle personality problems and started me on what has been an important part of my life work.

I used to go down to Princeton and talk over the new Princeton plan with friends. Each trip was more dismal than the preceding. The fight was on between Wilson and the old regime. I knew men in both camps, and the flat contradictions baffled me.

"Wilson's a fool."

"He's the greatest force in American education."

"He loses friends faster than he makes them."

"His manners are vile."

"He's the most gracious gentleman I ever met."

A dozen people told me stories like this: "I had an appointment with Wilson. When I entered, he eyed me grimly and said nothing. I told him what I had to say and waited for his comments. He scowled in silence, muttered a few words, and walked out. I wondered how I had offended him. He was obviously angry."

A neighbor told me: "I was passing the Wilson home as he

came out. We walked along, chatting about nothing in particular. He was charming, as usual. Then, at a cross street, without touching his hat or apologizing or explaining, Wilson suddenly frowned and turned abruptly up the side street."

IN 1919 I began to work with shell-shocked Army officers who were having a tough time returning to the world of business. Here was one who had broken almost every bone in his body and had lived to resume his old job with hardly any mental upset. Here was another whose injuries were trivial. If he carried a cane he could get around easily. But he loathed the cane. He seemed to regard it as a public confession of weakness. He was forever trying to do without it. Worse yet, he strove to walk without a limp. The strain was terrible. He insisted that life was empty for a cripple. Within two years he killed himself.

I reached two conclusions. Many people are better off with grave handicaps than with trifling ones. The grave handicap releases copious energies. The trifling handicap seems to stir the person too feebly to open up the big valves of nervous and mental power. Then, too, people often try to mask the petty handicap, which leads to further complication of the personality.

STUDY of personality leads naturally to a study of the living habits of people, and one day Dr. Lenna Means, a physician authorized to spend a small grant, came to my office and said: "I want you to investigate the women's shoe trade. We get more complaints about shoes than about everything else put together."

I ran through stacks of pitiful letters. Farm wives, working girls, schoolteachers, all asking where they might get shoes that didn't torture them.

We held meetings with manufacturers, retailers, and orthopedic surgeons. Most experts declared that there were plenty of good designs, that women complain of their shoes when they ought to complain of neglecting their feet. "For the sake of looking stylish, women will endure the torments of hell," commented a large retailer. Bad habits in standing and walking and slight carelessness in buying shoes that almost fit—but don't quite—combine to cause headaches, indigestion and neurasthenias. The shoe trade and the public health agencies, they said, ought to get together and open foot clinics.

Dr. Means suggested that I talk this idea over with others and she sent me to an orthopedic shoemaker, the best in the business.

As I entered his shop a warm blend of leather, foot oil, beeswax and old furniture assailed my nostrils. In the rear the shoemaker was fitting monstrous shoes on a crippled boy.

When the boy had gone I told the shoemaker about the suggested plan. He nodded.

"Of course there should be such clinics," said he. "What needless suffering might be prevented!"

"You feel much of it is needless?"

"Most of it. Half comes from ignorance, half from foolish pride."

"The ignorant we can educate in clinics, can't we?" I remarked. "But perhaps we must leave the proud to their fate."

"Yes! Yes! To their fate!" His eyes widened. He was seeing something far away. "The curse of keeping up appearances! It's far more terrible in a man than in a woman. Especially in a man of great power. I've seen its havoc. . . ."

He moved toward a tall cabinet and from an upper shelf brought down a plaster foot, covered with dust.

"What do you make of this?" He thrust it into my hands and edged me up to the window.

It seemed like an ordinary plaster model. Yet, as I eyed it, I did seem to detect slightly irregular proportions. The shoemaker thrust at me a large X-ray plate. "Study it. It's the same foot."

Here the irregularity was plainer. "Now," said the shoemaker with a gleam, "look at this." He handed me an old shoe. I ran my fingers over the inside. It was as soft as down. Here and there odd little reinforcements had been built in with such skill that they were scarcely noticeable. It was wonderful art.

"Seeing it on the wearer's foot," I said, "not one in a thousand would ever notice it."

"Yet the wearer noticed it always," said the shoemaker. "He was furious at it, all his life long. His pride was terrible. How he hated to appear different from other men! How he fought to keep up appearances! Until he grew too old and too sick to care for himself, he'd admit nobody—not even his own family—to the room while I was there trying to ease his pain. He wouldn't permit me to come to his front door. I had to go around to the back entrance. I couldn't tell who I was. I just left my name.

"He'd often scowl at me, as if I were to blame for his trouble. Once I hurt him. He kicked me. But I wasn't angry. I know some people can't control themselves when the pain comes. Sometimes I'd work for hours over a new shoe, while he clenched his fists until the knuckles turned white. He'd collapse on his divan. I'd pack the extra shoes in my valise and slip out the back door. Yes, Doctor, he wouldn't allow me to wrap them up in paper or carry them in a shoe box. I had to put them in a valise, so that nobody would ever know."

The shoemaker actually wept. He groped to his old roll-top desk, fished into a pigeonhole and hauled out a package of old letters.

"After he had lost his temper, he'd write me a letter. I kept them all. They have made my life worth while."

He placed the packet in my hands. I was torn between surprise at his sincere tears and bewilderment over the mystery of false pride. I untied the string, and the world roared around me. I went slightly dizzy. To this day, I have a vivid mental picture of those letters. That first letter ran something like this:

The White House . . . No date.

     I am sorry to have been so disagreeable yesterday. But you understand. You have helped me much. I am grateful. This last shoe will work out all right.
              Sincerely,
                    WOODROW WILSON

The next letter:

     Please come tomorrow at five, without fail. The shoe troubles me much. It must be changed immediately.
              Sincerely,
                    WOODROW WILSON

And the next:

     I must reassure you that my bad manners of yesterday meant nothing. You have been more than kind. I realize how much you have done for me.
              Sincerely,
                    WOODROW WILSON

A score more. Every letter was written on White House stationery in longhand, every envelope addressed by Wilson himself.

I knew what the shoemaker saw that made him weep. But he didn't know what I was seeing.

I SAW A MAN walking along a college street, stopping in pain, then turning swiftly and going home, there to stay until he could walk in comfort.

I saw a man—his face taut and grim—abruptly leave committee meetings, to the consternation of all those who did not know, as I did, the havoc overstrained nerves and muscle fibers can work on the human mind.

I saw a man try to wrestle with Lloyd George and Clemenceau at Versailles, never suspecting that the little Welshman had found how easy it was to override him simply by wearing him down during the day to a point of desperation at which he could neither think nor talk.

I saw history in those letters.

People Leave
Skulls with Me

by Loren C. Eiseley

As AN archaeologist I have a number of skulls in my possession. I can see four on the shelf above me and I know of two that are hidden in my filing cabinet. But I couldn't have taken old Mr. Harney's skull even if he had offered it to me.

It was from his family that I first got a hint of his story. "He keeps her in the china closet," one of them told me, "right with the dishes."

"The skull of Aunt Melvina," explained a grandson. "He never buried her."

"Oh?" I said, puzzled and tactful.

"He's curious about your work," another relative said. "We think maybe you could persuade him to give the skull to you. We don't like having her there. It isn't proper."

"It WAS barbed wire finished our world," Mr. Harney said. He was 80 years old, and the skull lay on the table before us. We sat silent, gazing out into the clear white sunlight of the southwestern desert. Eighty years, I thought. Years of smoking pistols and Apaches riding fast through narrow arroyos.

Though the white man has taken it, that vast and ominous landscape will never be rid of the ghosts of its last owners— the Apaches. It is their bones that lie on nameless peaks and in the red clay of the washes. Cochise, Victorio, Nana and Geronimo will haunt it always. In the '70s many men died here. Dozens of others were never accounted for—the desert swallowed them up. Old Mr. Harney knew: he had been one of the missing.

"You have lived a long life," I said.

The old man sighed, and began talking—the merest wisp of a sound that seemed to come out of the grass beside us.

"Six years in that valley after the haul from Texas, and me a youngster of ten. Mother dead on the trail. Her younger sister, Aunt Melvina, raised me—the old man meanin' well but ridin' most of the time. It took plenty ridin' to hold things together without the wire.

"Sure, we knew there was Apaches in the hills. But people had a way of stickin'"—he paused and reached out as if to touch the nearest blue hill—"as though they liked somethin' there—the air, maybe, so clear, or all that land at sunset, or maybe the feel of it, no fence from Texas to the Big Horns.

"Melvina was young and pretty with hair like the sheen on a blackbird's feather, and as good to me as my own mother. Young enough to play and imagine things the way a kid will. When my father was gone she used to play in the yard with me. Aaahh"—the old man got out something between a sigh and a groan—"it didn't last long.

"One night Pa didn't come home. Nobody knows what that means any more. The miles of darkness creeping in, and a woman and a kid sittin' in a shack waitin' for a man that ain't comin' back no more. You sit there and you dassn't light the light for fear of drawin' 'em. And all the time you know they know about you, and it's no good, they'll take their time.

"They got us in the morning, in the first light, with Melvina standin' out there lookin' for Pa. One of 'em just picked her off out of the bushes. I'm old, but sometimes I see it like now, just me with my hand at my mouth, and that shot. She stood there a minute all young and pretty with her hands stretched out to me. And all that love flowed up in her a minute and held her as if she wouldn't fall, and I ran toward her not thinkin' of anything except, as a kid will, that in the circle of such love I must be safe.

"And then she just gave a little sigh and that light went out of her and she pitched face down into a clump of prickly pear. They took me then, squalling and kicking, and put me on a horse. After that I was an Apache till I was 15."

The faded old eyes turned slowly over the whole compass of the horizon as though they remembered every peak and gully. "We rode into Old Mexico. They was Victorio's men. And I learned to be an Apache. Ride, shoot, steal. Live on nothing. Trust nobody, and keep ridin'—keep ridin'. South of the border, north of the border, it was all the same.

"Apaches! Y'know, son, that's a joker. We wasn't Apaches. We was a way of life. Half the kids in camp was stolen. Most of 'em Mexicans, raised Apaches. It was the only way to keep our strength up."

He paused, searching his memories. "In the end I didn't hate them. I was beginning to look at it the way they did, and to nurse the same feelings. I'd been shot at a lot and seen Indian families and kids I knew disappear. I would have stayed with them, I guess. I spoke the language by then." He stopped and whispered to himself a moment in syllables that were not English. Then he went on.

"Victorio must have thought different. Either that or he'd taken a shine to me—I never knew. He was a great warrior; Geronimo was nothing compared to him. When I was 15 we were sitting on our horses one day looking down into a little town from the hills. I could see people in the streets and smoke in chimneys. We watched it like animals must watch people—curious and sharp and wild, ready to vanish at the least sign of danger.

"Victorio edged his horse up beside me. 'Those are your people,' he said soft and low, and searching my face with his eyes. 'Do you remember?'

"And I looked at him, and suddenly the face of Melvina came to me and I said, 'Yes, I remember.'

"And he nodded, a little sad, and said, 'They are your people. Go down to them.'

"'My people,' I said, and stopped. It came to me that all the people I had were Apache, and that I was Apache, too.

"Not a muscle of Victorio's face moved. 'They are your people,' he said, pointing. 'We killed your father and the black-haired one. The white men will take care of you. You are not one of us.' He whirled his horse. I never saw him again.

"After a little I picked my way down and spoke some words of English. It was slow work, like an old hinge squeaking. People came up and stared at my rags and at the pony."

Harney paused, considering. "I got to be a white man. It was really about the same life: ride, shoot, kill. No difference, really, to amount to anything. Not then, anyhow."

His eyes came almost shut against the midday heat shimmer

out on the flats and I was afraid he was going to sleep. I pushed the skull toward him. "The skull, Mr. Harney. You promised to tell me about the skull."

His eyes opened a little way. "Aahh," he said again in that voice I was beginning to learn meant something hurt him. "It was afterward, sometime, that the thought came to me. I rode back to the old place. Nobody had been there all those years. And I found her—a few little bits of white bone, and the skull in a drift of sand with the prickly pear grown over it.

"Then it came on me I should bury her—and she out in the heat and dust and among bone-cracking coyotes so long. But what was there to bury, really? And besides, this is a big wide land where you see miles as long as you can see at all. Every day of your life you see that way. And it is hard to be underground afterward.

"In the end I knew I couldn't bury her there. She was the only kin I had, so I took her up carefully and rode back with her. I figured maybe I'd have it done in a proper ceremony with a churchyard and a preacher to ease it a little. But I kept putting it off and getting that feeling that if I did bury her she would go away; that she wouldn't be real any longer. When I settled here finally I kept Melvina safe in the china closet. She never had to be afraid any more, and she could look out through the glass.

"I'm a grown man, but that I did not get over—though I know all's dark in the grave and this is cold bone on the tabletop. I have a wife and sons, but this I will not bear—that they should put her under the ground with me."

By way of comfort I said quickly, "She will not want to look through the glass at strange faces. Let her go with you. One can stay too long in the sun."

"Aahh," he said, and took her into his hands. "It's plain you are not one of the open people, or you would not say that. It's the wire." His voice subsided once more to a thin whisper. "It's the wire that's made a difference. No wire from Texas to the Big Horns. It was all space and bright sun."

I LEFT old man Harney with his burden. He had assumed a personal responsibility that was not transferable.

Psychic Gifts

Who Saved John Kle?

by John Kle

IT HAPPENED so fast I didn't know what hit me. It was late in the afternoon of June 30, 1975; my friends Peter and Bart and I were sailing on Long Island Sound, plunging along in six-foot seas, surging before a 20-knot wind, the tail of Hurricane Amy. Suddenly a line tangled on the foredeck and, as I went forward to free it, a huge wave hit our stern, slamming our little boat to starboard. I went up in the air and when I came down, there was no deck beneath my feet and I fell straight into the water. I felt the shock of cold water on my flesh. I was not wearing a life jacket and, as the stern of the boat disappeared behind a huge comber downwind, I was filled with fear and the realization that, after 20 years of sailing, I was face to face with death.

I could see Bart and Peter struggling to bring the boat into the wind, but by the time she responded they were 80 yards away and I was just a speck in the angry waves. As I topped each wave, I could see them, searching, and I waved my plaid shirt in the air, hoping that they would spot that tiny speck of color in the heavy seas. They beat up toward my left. I could see Bart on the bow searching for me as Peter struggled with the helm. Winds gusting to nearly gale force screamed in my ear; whitecaps slapped me in the face. I think: *They must see me now*. But they don't. The boat disappears from sight. I am alone. I think: *It is my time to die*.

31

Quickly, I discarded my sneakers and shirt. I remembered a trick from lifesaving class and made a float by tying knots in the legs of my jeans and filling them with air. Two 360-degree turns on the crest of waves revealed that I was near the middle of the Sound, about four miles from Long Island. It was now about 7:30 p.m. with two hours of daylight left. I must make a decision: Which shore? Maybe it is a homing instinct, but I strike out for Long Island, where my wife Debbie and I live. The thought of Debbie somehow eases the reality of my situation. Momentarily, fear leaves and confidence enters me as I set to the task: *Save yourself, because no one can find you in this storm.*

THE PANTS FLOAT leaks its trapped air, but I manage to refill it twice before abandoning my jeans. Fatigue is setting in. Fear returns. Cold is the enemy. Already her icy fingers grip at my spine. Breaststroke, sidestroke and breaststroke again. At the top of each wave, a whitecap slaps me in the face and I battle the wind. I try to float on my back, but a whitecap washes over my face and I swallow a couple of gulps of water. Salt burns my lungs and my body contracts as I gasp for air. I am drowning; the water I've loved all my life is trying to kill me. *Stay calm, don't fight, work with the elements.*

My body responds, I'm okay. I think of Debbie, and just thinking of her brings new energy. I realize how much I don't want to leave her.

The sun is getting lower in the sky and the light is turning gold. I watch the changing sky while I do the endless sidestroke. This may be my last sunset; I am taken in by its beauty, blown clean by the high winds. The faint noise of a motor comes from somewhere. Turning, I see a small plane directly overhead. I wave, but the pilot doesn't see me.

I have been using the Empire State Building to gauge my progress, and there has been little. *Dear God, I've never asked You for anything before, but please help me now.* This small prayer seems my only hope.

As I keep working, new energy comes—from somewhere. There is perhaps 15 minutes of light left, and still so far to go. But I decide that if I die, it will only be after a fight, after I have given my all.

AT DUSK, I notice a small object in my path: a float for a lobster pot. It is a small miracle that I have swum straight to this tiny lifesaver. Ten yards to either side and I would have missed it. I grab onto it and take a desperately needed 30-second rest. The float is not spliced to the line, but tied. If only I can untie the knots that hold it captive! My numb fingers work at the knots, stiff with salt water. At last, reluctantly, the knots come apart. The float is mine as night engulfs me.

This tiny friend tucks under my arm like a football and barely floats my chest. Now, I can rest occasionally. I take a bearing from a bright light on Long Island shore—it looks to be about three miles away—and start out again with renewed strength and confidence. I swim endlessly, changing the buoy from side to side. I can rest only for a few seconds before my arms and legs become stiff with cold and fear makes me move on. I have never been so cold. Looking west at the lights of the Empire State Building, I can see that I am making progress, and from her bright lights I feel a new energy fill me. I estimate it is 10 p.m.

The blackness is suddenly pierced by the powerful beam of a Coast Guard searchlight. It shoots right over me; then a boat passes no more than 100 yards away. Looking around the horizon, I see the lights of a half-dozen Coast Guard and police boats and three helicopters as they search the waters for me with their powerful lights and dropped flares. I know that Peter and Bart are on one of the boats, and knowing that they are looking gives me additional strength.

Suddenly, the water around me explodes with light from a flare. I turn to wave at a helicopter hovering only 75 yards away and swallow the water spewing from a whitecap that hits me in the face. I lose the buoy in a coughing spasm. I cannot breathe. Then my hand retrieves the buoy and gathers it to my chest. *Stay calm. Don't panic.* Once more I can breathe. But leg cramps seize me, and I lose another full minute to the pain. I can feel my neck and lower spine starting to freeze. *Keep moving, or you will die.* Again, from somewhere, energy comes, and my tired legs start to kick. I start a rhythm: two strokes, breathe; two strokes, breathe. I'll hold this pace until the cold wins her battle and my fingers freeze and drop the tiny buoy. Then death. *Oh, God, I don't want to die.* Another surge of energy comes up from some strange, deep place, and it keeps me moving somehow—muscles on automatic. *Debbie, I need you.*

MY LEG HITS GROUND. I don't have the strength to rejoice but only to keep my forward momentum up the rocky, low-tide beach. I get stiffly to my feet and, clutching the buoy, I stumble toward a nearby house with lights in the windows. I can't feel the ground beneath my feet; I have lost all sense of my body.

My numb hand turns a doorknob; the door is not locked. I go in, out of the killing wind, and call: "Sir, I'm in your living room!" The owner appears, and when he sees my ash-white form, he runs to get blankets. He moves me in front of the stove, feeds me soup. It is now 12:30 a.m. I get my story out through chattering teeth so he can call the police and tell the search boats that I have made it ashore. Soon Debbie arrives and takes me home: home to warmth, love, security, the future.

SHORTLY AFTER the newspapers reported my story, I received a phone call from Buck, another of my sailing friends. He was very excited as he recounted the following incident:

"On the night you fell in the water, my wife and I were driving past the Empire State Building. We noticed a parking space right in front. Neither of us had ever been to the top of the Empire State, so we parked and went up. It was around ten o'clock. I pointed to the black void of Long Island Sound. 'That's where John and I went sailing last week,' I told Sue. Still talking of you, we put a dime in the binoculars and looked out into the dark sea where you were swimming right then."

As I listened to him, once more I felt myself taking my bearings from the lights of the Empire State Building. I remembered the warmth, strength and guidance those lights had given me. Had I perhaps been feeling the energy Buck and Sue were sending out to me?

A few days later, I received a letter from another close friend, Hitch, who was vacationing in the Caribbean. It was written June 30. He had been sitting on the beach just before writing me, and had suddenly been consumed by overpowering thoughts of me. There was no way he could have known that, more than 2000 miles away, I was fighting for my life. Again, I was transported back to that horrible blackness, to my desperate pleas for help, and to my hopeless feelings and fears, followed by the inexplicable confidence that kept coming back again and again to fight off my terror, and to keep me going. That energy was coming from somewhere: perhaps from that first genuine prayer I'd ever offered, or from those faraway Caribbean waters, or from the top of the Empire State Building, or from Peter and Bart, aboard a search boat—or from my small house in Sea Cliff, where Debbie was waiting.

Was I being tested that night—or protected?

I was still pondering that question when my friend Hitch came to visit us ten days later. He listened quietly to my tale, then went into the kitchen with Debbie to help her with preparations for dinner. A few minutes later he came dashing back into the living room, wild-eyed, with a frightened Debbie in tow.

"Look," he said, "you won't believe this, but the week before you fell in the water, I had a nightmare in which I kept seeing the numbers 9, 7 and 8, over and over. They woke me up, and each time I dozed off again they reappeared: 9, 7, 8. The experience frightened me so much that I told my sister about it. She urged me to forget about it, and I did, until just now."

He and Debbie kept staring at me. I asked what this was all about, whereupon Debbie went out to the kitchen and reappeared with the buoy that had saved my life. The small registration numbers carved into that buoy read 978.

Dorothy Allison's Psychic Eyes

by Joseph P. Blank

HE DIDN'T know what to expect when he walked up the steps to Dorothy Allison's house in northern New Jersey the evening of November 8, 1975. Two days before, Charles Little Eagle's 18-year-old daughter had vanished. Although he had reported her missing to the police, he felt desperate to do more. A friend had told him about Mrs. Allison's unusual ability.

For a few seconds after Little Eagle explained why he had come, Dorothy said nothing. A series of "pictures"—as if she were flicking a TV set on and off—flashed into her mind. With words tumbling over each other in her haste to tell everything seen, she said:

"Your daughter is safe. She is living in a filthy house with a red door. The number of the house is 106, 186 or 168. The name of the man with whom your daughter ran away has two r's in it. Like Harry. The location of the house will be found before January 21. But your reunion with your daughter should take place on January 21, maybe January 22. One more thing. You're going to become a grandfather."

Dorothy is a short, energetic housewife who loves cooking, doesn't at all mind cleaning, and thinks that shopping at the supermarket is fun. She is direct, candid, enthusiastic, affectionate.

She is also psychic. She can see beyond the scope of her knowledge and experiences. During the past years she has cooperated with scores of police departments to help locate missing persons. She also has answered the pleas of numerous families who have sought her help in locating a loved one. She refuses money for her efforts. "If I have been blessed with this gift," she says, "it would be wrong to use it for anything but humanitarian purposes."

In the Little Eagle disappearance, the police concluded there was no foul play. Since the girl was 18 they could not force her to return home, even if she was located. The father asked Dorothy if she would go out and try to find his daughter. She couldn't; she had a severe cold and, soon after, contracted pneumonia.

Little Eagle retained private investigator Charles Delahanty, who, after several weeks, came up with nothing. Then, in early January 1976, Delahanty visited Dorothy, now recovering from her illness. "Pick me up next Tuesday morning," she told him, "and we'll go look for the girl."

In the car with Delahanty and a colleague she said, "Let's go to New York." "Why?" the investigator asked. She answered, "That's where the girl is." Delahanty could see a wasted day ahead of him.

As they entered Manhattan, Dorothy pointed her finger and said, "Go that way." (She has no sense of direction. She can't even direct a stranger to her home.) For nearly three hours she guided the investigators in zigzag fashion through lower Manhattan, then deep into Brooklyn. Suddenly she said, "We have to look for something connected with taxis. And something connected with a President's name."

They came to Monroe Street. "Go around the corner," Dorothy said. "The girl is in a house on the next street." Delahanty muttered to his colleague, "This woman is out of it."

"There's the house," Dorothy exclaimed, pointing to a run-down tenement. It had a reddish-hued front door. The number was 186. On the first floor was a small store-front office that took calls for a taxi service. Delahanty was astonished.

They entered the building and talked with the woman who ran it. She stated that the girl had never been there. Outside, Dorothy told the investigators, "The girl is in there." Indeed she was, it was later learned, hiding under a bed.

On January 21, the father telephoned Dorothy and said, "Let's go to that house and get my daughter. You told me it would be today or tomorrow that I would see her."

"Not today," she replied. "I don't want to be involved in an accident. I'll go with you tomorrow."

The father couldn't wait. He and the two investigators began driving to New York. En route, a car skidded out of control on the icy highway and plowed into them. Fortunately, the accident, which demolished Delahanty's car, only bruised the occupants.

On the following day, Dorothy accompanied them. They found the girl at the house, living with a man named Harris (the two r's). She was pregnant, having conceived *after* Dorothy had told the father that he would become a grandfather. (Precognition is not unusual with Dorothy. On seeing a picture, she does not know if it applies to the past, present or future.)

The girl was confused about returning to her father's home. Dorothy suggested a cooling-off period, during which the girl would live with her and her husband, Bob, a supervising construction engineer. "We have plenty of room and we'd love to have you," she urged. The girl agreed. After a few months with the Allisons, she returned to her parents' house, before deciding to join the father of her child and build a life of her own.

Generosity and compassion are part of Dorothy's nature. Her parents not only raised 13 children, but also cared for a boy whose mother had died during his birth. "We were taught to care about one another and share what we had," Dorothy recalls. "That is why I find this work with missing persons so painful, yet so satisfying. When I meet parents of a missing child, I feel their anguish. When I look for that child, it is as if I am looking for one of my own."

Dorothy has known since childhood that she is psychic— her mother was, also—but she has no explanation for her clairvoyance and she sees no point in speculating about it. Her involvement with the police began unexpectedly at 6 a.m., December 3, 1967, when she awoke from a dream. She had seen a young boy dead in a pipe connected with a river. The vision nagged her day after day. Finally, she reported what she had "seen" to the Nutley, N.J., police. The police chief told her that five-year-old Michael Kurcsics had drowned in the Third River at about 8 a.m. (her dream occurred two hours earlier) on December 3 and his body had not been recovered. She hesitatingly told the chief that she was psychic. He wasn't impressed: the tragedy had been reported in local papers.

But patrolman Donald Vicaro, standing nearby, knew the Kurcsics family, and wanted very much to find their son's body. "Can you tell me something more?" he asked Dorothy. "Neither a picture nor any description of the child has appeared in the papers."

"Yes, I see more. Over his polo shirt, which had a religious medal pinned to it, he wore a green snowsuit. His mother is out of town. One more thing about Michael: his shoes are on the wrong feet."

Vicaro found the description of the outer clothing accurate. Then he telephoned Mr. Kurcsics. Did he know Dorothy Allison? No, never heard of her. Were Michael's shoes reversed? He didn't know: the child had dressed himself that morning. Was Mrs. Kurcsics at home? No.

Maybe Dorothy *did* have psychic powers, Vicaro thought. He asked if she would try to help him find the body. She eagerly agreed. At the bank of the river where Michael had fallen in, she kept repeating that she saw the body in a pipe. But the only pipes Vicaro knew of that related to the river were storm drains through which water flowed out into the river, so how could a body be carried from the river *into* the pipe? Vicaro then asked her to place herself mentally near the body and tell him what was directly in front of and behind her. She answered, "Water in front and behind."

"Are you standing in water?"

"No."

Vicaro concluded, "Either she's nuts or I'm nuts." He speculated that an expert in hypnosis might draw more specifics from Dorothy. Inquiries led him to Dr. Richard Ribner, a New York City psychiatrist, who put Dorothy into a semi-hypnotized state. Completely relaxed, she saw the figure 8 and a parking lot.

During subsequent days she told Vicaro that she saw a school with a fence around it, a gray house, a set of offices with gold lettering on a door, and a factory behind it. On February 7, Vicaro walked into the police station and was told that Michael Kurcsics' body had been found in Bleachery Pond, which was fed by the Third River, about three miles from where the boy had fallen in.

Vicaro drove to the pond. "The entire situation was awesome," he says. "It was actually two ponds, separated by a narrow strip of land. When I stood on that strip there was water in front of me and behind me. From where I stood I could see Public School No. 8 with a fence around it, a gray house and an office with gold lettering on the door. Behind the office was a plant with a parking lot. And Michael—he was wearing a polo shirt with a religious medal pinned to it. And the shoes were on the wrong feet."

Vicaro learned that at the time Michael drowned, a construction company had laid large pipes in the stream that fed into the pond. The pipes were used as a foundation for an improvised bridge. It was quite likely that Michael's body was caught for a time with debris in one of the pipes.

"Dorothy is not always correct," Dr. Ribner explains. "She may get a picture of a car and see 269 on the license plate. If that sequence of numbers doesn't pan out, then 692 or 296 should be checked. Or the numbers might apply to an address or a telephone number."

To Dr. Ribner, a most surprising display of Dorothy's powers occurred in his office. She and two detectives had asked for an appointment. When they arrived, a patient was sitting in the waiting room. After the psychiatrist admitted the three to his office and closed the door, Dorothy said, "Richard, that young man out there has a gun and is contemplating suicide. He has tremendous potential and, once he gets over his illness, he will become very successful."

"I knew the patient was severely depressed and suicidal," Dr. Ribner recalls. "When I asked him about the gun during the session, he conceded that he did have it and intended to use it. I persuaded him to give it up and to continue working on his problems. Today, he is an industrial designer and is doing fine."

When Dorothy is wrong, the picture will sometimes have a startling aspect to it. Detective Salvatore Lubertazzi of the Nutley police department once mentioned to her that a child had been murdered that day.

"Look for a nurse," Dorothy advised.

"You're wrong," Lubertazzi said. "We know that the child was killed by the mother, who is totally deranged. She's a school teacher."

Within a few hours, the mother, Maria Horst, was in custody. "But then I learned something interesting," Lubertazzi told me. "A couple of miles from the home of the mother lived a nurse. Her name also was Maria Horst; and the two women resembled each other."

Some families of missing persons have found Dorothy a rock of support during their ordeals. On May 15, 1976, 14-year-old Susan Jacobson failed to appear for dinner at her Staten Island, N.Y., home. By morning, her parents knew in their hearts that she was dead. Susan had no reason to vanish voluntarily—none. The police told the Jacobsons that Susan undoubtedly was a runaway and the case would be turned over to the Missing Persons Squad.

After three weeks of searching for their daughter, the Jacobsons heard about Dorothy Allison, and the girl's mother, Ellen, telephoned her. Dorothy had just gone through gum surgery, and her mouth and face were terribly sore. But she was caught by the pain and urgency in Ellen's voice. "Give my husband the directions to your house," she said, "and we'll leave in ten minutes." She had never visited Staten Island.

"What do numbers 2, 5, 62 mean to you?" Dorothy asked, writing out the numbers, after their arrival.

"That's Susan's birthday. February 5, 1962."

"What about 408 or 405?"

"That's the approximate time of her birth."

"I see that Susan's body is on this island. The letters 'M A R'—do they mean anything to you?" Ellen shook her head. "She is near those letters. And from that place you will see two sets of twin church steeples, two bridges and a burned-out car. Maybe we'd better talk to the police." The police, according to Ellen, made little attempt to conceal their disdain at being offered clues by a psychic.

With relatives and friends, William Jacobson drove around Staten Island, looking for a scene that fitted Dorothy's description. On the sixth day he chanced on a huge boulder, which bore the large, red-printed letters, "M A R." To his astonishment, he could see a burned-out car, two bridges and two sets of dual church steeples across the bay in New Jersey. Throughout this area were some 50 well-like shafts that had been used for shipbuilding in World War I. Most of the shafts contained water.

He drove Dorothy to the site. She believed Susan's body was there, but it was such a large area—about 1½ square miles—that she suggested William ask the police to bring in bloodhounds. The police refused: "We deal with facts, not psychics."

During the horror of the ensuing months, the Jacobsons leaned heavily on the Allisons. The couples exchanged visits.

Ellen was on the telephone with Dorothy several times a week. "Were it not for Dottie, William and I would have had nervous breakdowns," Ellen says.

On March 23, 1978—22 months after Susan disappeared— three boys were hunting for muskrats in some shipbuilding shafts from which water had drained. In one—a shaft that William had tried to search but was stopped by water—they found a 55-gallon drum containing Susan's remains. Six weeks after the discovery, an 18-year-old youth who had known Susan was charged with her murder; he was convicted and sentenced to 22 years to life in prison.

"It was finally over when her body was found and I felt a sense of relief," Ellen says. "I got the only thing I knew I could have—the chance to give Susan a proper burial."

Sometimes Dorothy is overwhelmed by the pain and sorrow of her discoveries. Once she stopped helping the police, but she found it was worse to live without using her power than to continue. "It is a gift," she says. And Dorothy knows that a gift must be returned, in some way, by giving.

The Night
My Number Came Up

by Air Marshal Sir Victor Goddard

I AM a professional aviator and, though I have experienced disaster by air, I am not given to premonitions of mishap. Yet as we were about to take off from Shanghai for Tokyo I was depressed.

After two years in command of the Royal New Zealand Air Force in the Pacific and two more administering British Air Forces in Burma and Malaya I was on my way home via Tokyo to say farewell to General MacArthur and other Americans with whom I had worked during the war. Admiral Mountbatten had loaned me his own plane, the *Sister Ann,* and her crew, both the embodiment of reliability.

My depression was due to a foreboding that I was about to carry into mortal danger all who flew with me, and to the knowledge that I could not, for want of justification, bid my passengers remain behind. As an air marshal, how could I possibly say that I'd been warned supernaturally?

It had happened at a party the previous evening in Shanghai. I was talking with my old friend Brigadier General John McConnell, USAF, when I heard two Englishmen behind me begin a conversation which caught my attention at once:

"Wasn't this party to welcome Air Marshal Goddard?"

"It certainly was. Why?"

"He's dead! Died last night in a crash."

The man spoke with a disconcerting tone of authority. I

43

turned slowly around. The man, a British naval commander, glanced quickly at my face and started as though I had hit him.

"My God!" he exclaimed with a gasp. "I'm terribly sorry! I mean I'm terribly glad—that is—how extraordinary! I do apologize! You see, I had a dream last night. It seemed so true."

I smiled. "I'm not dead yet, Commander. What did you dream? Where did it happen?"

"On a rocky, shingly shore, in the evening, in a snowstorm. It was China or Japan. You'd been over the mountains in cloud. Up a long time. . . . I watched it all happen."

"What sort of plane was I in?"

"An ordinary sort of transport. Possibly a Dakota." *(Sister Ann* was a Dakota.)

"What about the crew in your dream—all killed too?"

"It was a shocking awful crash," he replied.

I was about to leave the commander when I decided to test him further on facts. What he had said about geography and terrain seemed to fit too well.

"Did your dream show you what sort of people I was traveling with?"

"Yes," he said, a little slowly. "An ordinary service crew and three civilians. Two men and a woman. All English."

"Thanks very much. That's quite a relief. I'm carrying no one but a service crew. No civilians. By the way, I don't know your name."

"Oh, I'm Dewing, from the *Crécy.* I'm in harbor here."

We chatted a while and moved apart. I never saw him again.

A few minutes later Seymour Berry of the London *Daily Telegraph* drifted up alongside me and said, "I'm anxious to get home and would like to catch a lift to Tokyo with you. Your pilot said it will be O.K. by him. Do you mind?"

With a feeling of shock, I replied, "Not at all. Plenty of room. I'm leaving at half past six in the morning." But in my heart I feared this acceptance of Berry as a passenger.

That same evening, George Alwyne Ogden, the British consul general, gave a dinner party for me. Ogden was questioning me about my journey when his Chinese butler handed him a radio message. Ogden passed it to me, saying, "I am sorry to impose upon you, but I wonder if you can possibly take me with you tomorrow?"

How could I refuse? The message was from the Foreign

Office; it was imperative that the consul general visit the British high commissioner in Tokyo as soon as possible.

I reflected: *That makes two civilians. Englishmen. But there's no woman. Anyway, what bosh, worrying about a stranger's nightmare.*

Before the meal was over, the butler again presented an envelope. Another radio message. Ogden said, "You'd better read it. It's from Gardiner, our representative in Tokyo."

"...I have no reliable conference stenographer," I read. "Most grateful if you could loan one for few weeks."

"Are you going to be able to help me on this too?" asked Ogden.

"I guess I can take him," I replied reluctantly. "That is, if he's a man!"

"Does that make a difficulty? He's bound to be a girl, I'm afraid."

Three civilians, one of them a woman.

THAT was a cheerless dawn at the Shanghai Airport. Consul General Ogden had brought Dorita Breakspear, a tall, fair girl about 20 who told me she had never flown before. "But I expect I shall survive," she said. Her trusting remark stabbed me, and I shivered in the chill breeze off the runways.

Squadron Leader Don Campbell, our captain, didn't look particularly cheerful.

"Morning, Campbell. Got a good weather forecast?"

"Not too bad, sir. About a hundred miles from Tokyo there may be a good deal of high cumulus—something like a front, perhaps. Should be about six hours' flight."

With that we went aboard, and shortly *Sister Ann* soared away over the sprawling city, set on her course for Tokyo or— Perish the thought! Dewing had said this thing would be in the evening in a snowstorm. We should be in Tokyo soon after lunch. I was dog-tired. After a while I fell asleep.

I could not have slept long when the bumpiness of cloud flying awakened me. I was breathing rather fast. We must be high. The starboard wing was searing through the mist; gray fragments seemed to be breaking away from the leading edge and flying away aft. Ice!

Dorita and Seymour were asleep. Consul General Ogden seemed distressed with his breathing: said he had a rotten cold in the head. Soon the light grew brighter. We were soaring blithely in blinding sunlight. But there, clinging to the shining metal of the great, flexing wings, I could see a thin layer of ice.

Campbell came aft and spoke to me in a low voice. "We shall have to keep above it. If we go through we shall get heavily iced again."

"Yes," I said. "I noticed that. We must be pretty high now."

"Seventeen thousand."

"No oxygen aboard?"

"No."

After a while Campbell came aft again. "We shall have to have another shot at going through it, sir. The cloud tops are still higher, and we are now at about 18,000. I expect it will be a bit bumpy."

In we went—into that swirling, darkening mist—and down.

Campbell throttled back a bit. Then I heard the *Crack! Thud!* of broken ice against the cabin—ice chunks flung off the propeller blades. It grew darker. My watch said 11:20. That would be only 12:20 Tokyo time. And that wasn't evening! But how long before the ice would cease to snap away and, instead, suddenly build up a great solid shroud?

But there was no snow. Surely Dewing had said there would be snow?

Once again those enveloping gray mists were suddenly flung aside. As if hurtling over a chasm, *Sister Ann* flashed into the dazzling blue among the towering, billowing cloud tops.

Ear pressures and quickened breathing told us we had climbed again to heights where oxygen is rare. The consul general and Dorita were ill and faint from lack of oxygen. I feared for their lives. They could hardly carry on much longer at that height.

Campbell came aft again, a little gray in the face from fatigue and anxiety, but carrying a smile and an air of quiet confidence.

"Aren't we above maximum ceiling for a Dakota?" I asked. "Couldn't we let down a bit steeper now to get to warmer layers? We must be getting light in fuel by now. That should lower the stalling speed if the ice keeps off. But you do it your own way, Campbell. I guess we shall come through all right." *Unless,* I thought to myself, *we hit that rocky seashore and shingle.*

Campbell smiled and said he would give it a go.

We started down. Once more began that plunging, jolting, heaving, that was to continue unabated for yet another four long hours. We bumped our way down, down, into the wet, cold base of that towering cumulonimbus cloud. How dark it grew! Then I heard that vicious *crack-crack* on the metal flanks of *Sister Ann*. Ice. Ice on the props again.

Then suddenly we were out of it—but nearly into something else! Those yellow lumps heaving there below were waves of the sea.

And now *it's snowing hard! What's the time? Three-thirty. Sea and snow. That was what Dewing had said it would be.* Below us we saw the blackness of a snow-flecked cliff, with broken waves lashing white anger at its feet.

The turbulence was the worst in my experience, and it seemed that *Sister Ann* might not withstand it for long. We followed the shore and after a while came over a bay. There, beside a rocky, shingly shore, lay a snow-covered fishing village. The beach was less than 300 yards of shelving shingle interspersed with rocks, and bounded at each end by black crags. No fit place to land.

Out we swung again to follow cliffs and breakers in that shallow, horizontal chasm of driven gray snow between cloud and surging sea. My watch, now at Tokyo time, said five past four. At that latitude it would be dark soon after five on a day like this.

Then we lost the cliff. Fearing to butt into another headland, Campbell held away for a while, then edged in again.

So it went. We lost the cliff. Found it again. Never a break. Never even a stretch of shore on which to crash-land.

It was getting gloomier all round us. If there was a sun anywhere, it must have set by now. A quarter to five. Cliffs, cloud, sea, snow, foam on the rocks, noise, turmoil, nausea, thickness in the head, pain in the ears, fatigue.

Suddenly the cliff ended again. Visibility improved a bit. *Here's a bay. A village in snow by the shore. Shingle, rocks. The village and bay we saw an hour or more ago. We must have flown all the way around an island and got back again.*

I loosed myself from my seat and gripped my way forward to the compartment.

"Let me see your map," I said to our navigator, Flight Lieutenant N. Anderson.

About 40 miles off the mainland there was an island something like the shape of a hand pointing. Sado, it was called.

"That's it," I said. "And that village must be Takachi."

Anderson looked, nodded. Then he said, "The nearest airfield is Tokyo, the other side of the mainland. That's nearly 200 miles, over the mountains and clouds in the dark. Not too good."

"And no gas," I replied.

That rocky, desolate shingle shore beside the breakers down there was our only possible destination. Just as Dewing had said. In snow and storm, in the evening.

I turned to Campbell. He looked at me, smiling and determined, as he said, "Bad show, sir, I'm afraid. If you agree, we must land on this little beach. No question of jumping for it—clouds too low and too much wind."

"Yes."

"Would you land wheels up or down?"

"I think you'd slide faster and farther," I said, "if you kept your wheels up and landed on your belly. But if you keep them down and don't crash the big rocks, we shall certainly turn over. What about keeping your wheels down ready to retract, and as we begin to slow up retract as quickly as you can?"

Campbell nodded, both hands strongly joggling the control column. He was sweating.

I went aft to do what I could to protect the bodies of my crew and my companions. Everyone but the skipper should come into the cabin to keep the tail down. We'd be safer there, and quicker out. All must fix themselves so that they could not be thrown, and be swathed in blankets, covered with mattresses.

And so I saw to their dressing up for this queer play with death; I, at any rate, was sure I was about to die.

When we were ready two crewmen staggered aft to open the door so we wouldn't be stuck inside. Off it came with a sudden roar as the full blast of snow-filled air burst in. There was a crash of china, cutlery and trays in the pantry.

The picture of what was going to happen in the next few minutes had been in my mind for the past 24 hours. Now I could hear, above the roar of air, the hiss-squeeze of the wheels going down. Then down went the flaps, and *Sister Ann* banked close to the northern cliff, nose down for landing. The engine roar subsided. I looked round at Ogden. He smiled in a tired, pain-racked way. I looked at Dorita. Her eyes were closed. I couldn't see Berry's face.

Banked over as we were, I could see the curving, shelving beach with its strewn, jagged rocks and a steeple of rocks at the end. Down we went, straightening out and flattening out at the same moment. Then the engine noise died out. High rocks sped blackly by to port.

Now we are for it.

A rippling, jingling sound began. Wheels ripping swiftly over shingle. It grew harsher. The deceleration began.

Let the wheels back, I prayed. But Campbell had. *Sister Ann* was flopping down.

Bang. . . . Bang! Cr-runch. . . . Oh, that stomach. Up! Somersaulting. Belly pull. Stop. Neck-break pain.

Hugeness hurtled by me, striking the back of my head. It was Ogden, seat and all.

Motion ceased. *Sister Ann* had stopped dead.

There was a stillness. Then the splashing flop and a hiss of breakers on the shingle . . . a quiet whistle of wind.

"My chair came off!" cried Ogden, almost apologetically.

Unstrapping, we began to laugh. I went forward to Campbell as he was coming aft. We met in the gangway and shook hands.

That night we sheltered in the little inn of Takachi. As I lay on the matted floor, I wondered whether Commander Dewing really had "seen" me, personally, in a state of total inanimation—dead. I must write to Dewing, I decided, before he forgets what he did dream.

Months later I got a reply:

I am horrified to hear about your crash. I remember our meeting and I vaguely remember that dream. No, I can't say that I actually saw you dead, but I certainly thought the crash was a killer. Glad it wasn't.

For my next crash I want no prior information. Quite spoils the enjoyment of flying.

ESP, Freddie and Me

by Esse Campbell

FREDDIE WAS SPECIAL from the beginning. I could not refuse him when he was handed to me, black and silky, in the supermarket parking lot one yellow-hot summer morning in Hollywood.

A couple approached me as I was carrying groceries to my car. "Ma'am," the young man said, "we watched you go in. We just know you're a cat person. We love him, but we can't keep him. Could you please give him a home?"

I smiled at their openness—and took the seven-week-old part-Persian in my hands, to look into his bright topaz eyes. We connected.

He would not break the gaze. He purred, telling me to take him. I looked at his crooked tail. Its cartilage had been malformed, so it had a bushy-squirrel sweep—crazy-looking on a little black cat.

"Of course I'll take him," I said, snuggling him against my face. I noticed that he smelled of talcum powder, and I knew they had taken care to make him irresistible.

I thanked them, feeling somewhat the plaything of unknown forces. Maybe I accepted the little black creature because of the conversation I had had the night before with a friend who was studying extrasensory perception—ESP.

Knowing that my tiger-striped cat, Sam, was missing, she had offered her help. She would show me a meditation ritual, she said, which might reach him through the use of psychic power. This power, she indicated, is possessed by all of us in varying degrees. If Sam were alive, she believed, a strong telepathic call would bring him back. If he were dead, another cat, of psychic bent, would come to take his place—quickly, perhaps within 24 hours.

She spoke with great conviction, yet I was skeptical at first. But she was a nice, normal woman, not given to spells, so I listened. Finally, hope and curiosity overcoming skepticism, I agreed to try her suggestion. The next morning, I felt I *had* to go to that supermarket.

I NAMED the new kitten Freddie. I soon learned he was trusting, baby-awkward with his outsized paws, and a music lover. "Rock-a-bye Baby," crooned as "Rock-a-bye Freddie," would zonk him into all-out naps, limp and luxuriating on my lap. He loved love, and expected it from everyone. With great gusto he welcomed my friends, and sat in each lap at living-room gatherings.

In no time he had locked himself into my life with a sensitivity so intense that I finally decided we somehow understood each other in an unusual way—perhaps on the ESP frequency that had apparently brought us together. His special reaction to my psychic friend, Janne, who had counseled me the night before he burst into my life, seemed to bear this out. He *knew* when she was coming to visit, and never left her side once she arrived.

King as well as clown, Freddie thought he owned the world. And so he did, for the 15 months that we lived in the Hollywood hills. Then I learned that I would have to move to New York, under circumstances allowing no room for him. With a deep sense of loss, I offered Freddie to Janne, but she could not take him until her elderly, terminally ill poodle died—a projected six to ten weeks. We agreed that, until then, she would place Freddie with Mary, a friend of hers who lived across town in Brentwood.

When Mary came to get Freddie the Saturday after Thanksgiving, I tried to be adult about the situation, and almost made it—except for the final moment of transfer, when Freddie's hurt and outrage undid me. That frightened accusatory look haunts me still. Born of total devotion, it begged me not to do this terrible thing. But, weeping, I let him go.

Then I threw myself into the happy first stage of my trip—a three-week visit with my daughter in Santa Cruz, Calif., to see her graduate from nursing school. My son flew in from New York, too, and there were wonderful, crowded days.

But, alone at night, tired, I thought about Freddie. I had betrayed him, rationalize as I might. All I could do was count on time to help. What I had *not* counted on was a strange, growing apprehension. On my last night in Santa Cruz, while idly watching TV, I found myself suddenly saying aloud, "Freddie, are you all right?"

I startled myself, since I don't normally do such things. But I had felt a weird pressure to say those words. Even stranger, I had then sensed Freddie's presence in his favorite position, cuddling under my right arm, head under my chin. It was so real, so strong, that my hand was already in the air to stroke him when I shook myself out of the spell.

The next morning, rather than drive to New York as originally planned, we three decided that I should sell my car in California, then fly east. That meant my returning to Los Angeles, where the car papers and a bigger market waited. Christmas was just days off, and suddenly it felt so right to be going back that I literally sang as I drove along Highway 101.

As soon as I got home, I called Mary. "How's Freddie?"

"I don't know how to tell you this," she said. "Freddie ran away the day after he got here." A visiting friend had held the front door open a second too long, she explained, and Freddie had run out—into an unfamiliar part of gigantic Los Angeles. She had hunted him for days. She kept apologizing. I kept forgiving her.

After I hung up, I stared out the window, stricken. No wonder I had felt him calling to me! I was frozen with guilt and despair.

I called Janne. She had known from the first, heartsick, unable to tell me. The next night, I had a nightmare about Freddie in great trouble. My phone woke me, and it was Janne—just coming to from the same nightmare! The coincidence was too great not to alarm us. She urged me to call her ESP teacher, a noted parapsychologist. He suggested that I go to the last place the cat had stayed and repeat the same meditation ritual I had used to get him the first time.

Minutes later, I was on my way to Mary's, with cat food and my old kitchen rug ripe with smells of home. I explained to Mary what I was up to, and asked if I could stay for 24 hours. She agreed, offering to join in if it would help. So did Janne, when I called her. At six that evening, then, there were three adult women ready to pool their psychic powers to find one little black cat. And suddenly none of us felt foolish.

By seven we had finished our meditations, drained. Through the long night, I listened for the smallest cat noise. By morning, hope was hard to hang onto. By 11 o'clock I was demoralized. *He's dead,* I told myself.

Then I felt it—a rush of excitement, a push to get to my feet and walk out the front door. I followed the urge, fighting to keep the rising tide of hope from blocking the receiving powers of my mind. I was led across the street, up a block, turned to the right, brought to a halt before a lane marked "Private." Conditioned response said: stop. ESP said: go in. I went. ESP said: call. "Here, Freddie," I called. Whistle. Call.

A woman's voice came from a house window. "Are you by any chance looking for a black cat?" she asked.

A 200-volt shock went through me. "Yes!" I cried out. "With a funny crooked tail!"

"That's the one!" she said.

Now she was running out to me, young and kind and happy. "I'm so glad!" she said. "I *knew* he belonged to someone. He's been around here for a month." Her little boy had found him and brought him home. He refused to enter their house. He showed up twice a day, begging for food. *Freddie begging!* Then he had run off and hidden again. *Freddie, this most people-loving cat, hiding alone!* She had worried about him, tied a note to his collar. She fed him scraps and milk. He would be back this evening. She would call me. She was so relieved!

I thanked her over and over. Her name was Mira Hoenig, and she had cared. "How lucky you waited till now to come," she said. "I was gone all morning." How could I explain that luck had nothing to do with it? I gave her my telephone number and left.

By four o'clock, I couldn't wait any longer. Cat food and kitchen rug in hand, I drove to Mira Hoenig's house. As I got out of the car, around the corner came Freddie—thin, drooping, luster and confidence gone, on his way to beg for food.

At the sight of him, I forgot that cats don't like being grabbed. I *had* to grab him, and hold him tight. Scared into shock, he tried to bolt. Then I showed him his food. He ate the whole can without seeming to draw a breath. Still stunned, he sat back and stared at me, clearly not believing I was really there.

I kept saying, "I'm so sorry, so sorry." I stroked him gently, then picked him up and carried him to the car. He looked it over warily. I set him on the kitchen rug on the front seat. He sniffed his territory. At last he believed. He rolled and purred and cuddled and kissed. If animals wept, he would have been crying—along with me.

I brought him to New York. And later, we moved to California, where Freddie is a beach bum. He will always be with me. As someone said, "That ESP stuff really works—if you're dumb enough to try it."

The Inexplicable Powers of Sam Benson

as told to Jhan and June Robbins

This is the first-person story of a small-town hardware dealer who was born with extrasensory perception (ESP), the apparently inexplicable power to learn of events by means other than the normal senses. Outwardly an ordinary American, he was embarrassed—and his wife was frightened and sometimes angry—when his strange powers took over. Because some people were disturbed by his mysterious gift and because he felt that publicity would hurt his business, he is here called Sam Benson, and certain other names in his story have also been changed.

IT OCCURRED one winter evening when I was seven years old. It was the first time I can remember being conscious that I could know things other people weren't aware of. My father was late coming home for dinner, and Mother was fretting. Without thinking, I explained to her that there had been a trolley accident, that Pop was all right but had stopped to help some people who were hurt, and was being treated to drinks by a man from the trolley company.

A little later, Pop came in—bruised, bandaged and a little tight. He said he'd been in a streetcar accident, but Mom didn't believe it. When I said that I'd seen the accident in my mind and that Pop was telling the truth, she said we'd made up the story together.

So I learned at the very beginning that it isn't necessarily good to have extrasensory perception, as it's called.

We were not a rich family. There were 11 of us, and at Christmas we each received one present. I soon realized that I could look at each box under the Christmas tree and tell what was in it. One year I looked at the box marked for my brother Fred and clearly got the word "mitt" in my head. "You're getting what you want—a baseball glove!" I whispered.

When Fred opened his package, however, it contained a pair of handknit wool mittens. Without a word he socked me in the eye.

Some things come to me that I don't pretend to understand. A number of years ago, for example, our daughters took piano lessons from a man named Fanelli, who came to the house every Thursday evening. One night I had a vivid half-dream in which I saw Mr. Fanelli struggling through a blizzard at the North Pole. He fell down and couldn't get up—his legs wouldn't move. In my dream I thought they were frozen.

That Thursday, Mr. Fanelli failed to show up. We learned that he had collapsed, paralyzed in both legs by spinal meningitis, at about the time I dreamed that he was crippled by freezing.

Persons who have psychic gifts can sometimes see into the future. This doesn't happen to me too often, but I will never forget an event that occurred a few years ago. I was at church, getting into my choir robe, as was a friend, Martin Engels, a house painter. Suddenly I looked at Martin and, in my mind, saw him lying still on the ground, covered by a paint-spattered drop cloth.

The image was so real that people tell me I turned pale and appeared shocked. The choir rehearsal proceeded, but our minister saw that I was disturbed. He took me aside and asked, "Something wrong, Sam?" I told him, with some embarrassment, of my conviction that something terrible was going to happen to Martin Engels. Three days later, Martin fell from a scaffold and was killed.

Since the event happened exactly as I foresaw it, could I have saved Martin Engels' life by warning him to stay off scaffolds? I don't know. But ESP has sometimes helped me protect my family from danger.

One night a few weeks ago, I woke up from a deep sleep, jumped out of bed and hollered, "I smell smoke!"

With my wife, Fran, I searched the house. There was no fire, and we went back to bed. About ten minutes later, however, I insisted, "There *is* a fire. It's at your mother's house!"

Fran looked at me incredulously. "Mother's house is eight miles away!" she said. But she dialed her mother's number anyway.

"Now, Mom, don't get scared," she said, "but Sam has some queer idea that your house is on fire. It was probably just a bad dream, but he says he can't go back to sleep until you check and call us back."

Fifteen minutes later the phone rang. Fran's mother had discovered a smoldering fire in the wall behind her kitchen range, and with a neighbor's help she had put it out. There was no more need for us to worry.

Our son Ted seems to have inherited some of my ESP qualities. I don't know whether a scientist would agree that Ted and I can read each other's minds, but we do something a lot like that.

Years ago, when Ted was only seven, he was already a fine swimmer. So Fran and I let him go swimming one day with friends in a nearby quarry. At about two o'clock that afternoon, I came down with a severe headache and felt sick at my stomach. Suddenly I saw an image of my son drowning. He was out in the middle of the quarry, his legs doubled under him. He had already gone under twice and was beginning to strangle.

I prayed: "Dear Heavenly Father, tell Ted to stroke with his arms—turn on his back. Tell him not to panic."

I left work and drove toward the quarry. I met Ted heading toward home on his bicycle. He said he'd been having fun swimming. After I asked him a few questions, however, he began to cry. "I had a scare, Pop," he said. "I got this awful bellyache. My legs just folded. I was out in the middle with about 50 feet of water under me. I went under. I swallowed water. I hollered, but nobody came to help me. So I turned on my back, and paddled with my arms to shallow water. I didn't really know what to do—something just told me."

Yet, there are many times when Fran and I wish that these powers would just go away. When I first took over the hardware store, for example, I discovered that ESP was damaging my business. Many times when customers came in the door I knew instantly what they wanted. I'd get a picture of ten pounds of nails, a roll of tape or a pair of lawn shears—and I'd have the items on the counter before the customer could open his mouth. If he had forgotten something, I'd remind him: "Your wife told you to buy a cushion for your porch chair."

A few people got sore. Quite a number became uneasy and started trading elsewhere—and I didn't know why. Then a friend taught me a lesson and, I guess, saved my business. When I saw him wheel into the parking space I knew he wanted a flyswatter, 15 feet of electric cord and ten light bulbs. I cut the cord off the reel and had everything waiting for him.

He leaned on the counter and said, "What's all that stuff?"

"Your order!" I said proudly.

"What order?" he asked. "I don't want to buy anything— I just dropped in to pass the time of day."

Then he burst out laughing. "I was coming in for those things, Sam," he said. "But you take all the fun out of shopping—and you're making some people nervous. When a man spends money, he has the right to give his own orders."

I took his advice. Slowly, people got over the idea that I was some kind of mind reader. I don't correct customers any more even when I know they are wrong. Not long ago a woman came in and bought a large quantity of plaster of paris. I knew— although she didn't tell me—that she really needed cement. She came back an hour later, very annoyed with herself, and exchanged the plaster for cement. I could have saved her the trip—but I've learned I can't afford to give advice.

What Do We Really Know About Psychic Phenomena?

by Laile E. Bartlett

• A MOTHER DREAMED that in two hours a violent storm would loosen a heavy chandelier which would fall on her baby's crib. She awoke her husband. "A silly dream," he said. "The weather is clear. Go to sleep!" But she brought the baby to her bed. In two hours a storm came up, and the light fixture fell on the crib.

• Eating lunch at school, a 13-year-old girl "heard" her little sister screaming. She ran home to find the child had cut her hand almost in half. She summoned the doctor, who arrived in time to save her sister from bleeding to death.

This is the world of Psi (psychic phenomena)—or ESP (extrasensory perception), as aspects of it are known. It has been blocked off from us by our conditioning. For decades we've been taught that what is "real" is only what our five senses perceive. But some scientists tell us that Psi is our new frontier. They see a future world where we can be in instant touch with others around the globe, hurdle time and space with a leap of the mind, know the future and past as well as the present, and cure our own ills through the power of the mind. Whatever the future brings, we are now in the midst of a great Psi explosion. The Parapsychological Association was finally accepted as a member of the American Association for the Advancement of Science in 1969. A few years ago the Psi SEARCH exhibit traveled to museums, universities and libraries, under the auspices of the venerable Smithsonian Institution. Documenting the scientific investigation of psychic phenomena with photographs and research material of the past 40 years, the exhibit attempted to evaluate what has been proved about Psi and what is speculation.

Psi is indeed controversial. It is an open invitation to charlatans who prey on confused and eager seekers. For many, it opens a closet they'd rather keep shut: "My dreams keep coming true. Am I going crazy?"

There has been small place for the psychic in the standard scientific world. Paul Kurtz, professor of philosophy at the State University of New York at Buffalo, speaks for many skeptical scientists when he says: "We are disturbed that only so-called positive results are published. The public rarely hears about negative findings, which are considerable." Stanley Krippner, chairman of the advisory committee of the Traveling Psi SEARCH exhibit, takes issue with Kurtz, saying, "In the ten years of our work in ESP and dreams at Maimonides Medical Center in Brooklyn, we published all our results, negative or positive. For many years parapsychologists have been the outcasts of science," he goes on to admit. "Fortunately, this is changing because of recent improvements in experimentation."

Pinning down psychic phenomena is a slow, exacting process. Because the whole field is on trial, serious Psi researchers are superstrict in their methods, and conservative in their professional reporting. Nonetheless, from their experiments here's what we do know:

People can and do communicate by means other than the five senses: telepathy.

Telepathy comes through in everyday incidents and serious warnings. According to studies made by Louisa Rhine of the Institute of Parapsychology in Durham, N.C., a waitress "gets the message" and hands a man his order before he gives it. A Texas teacher breaks a rule and leaves her students to be near the telephone. It rings: "Come at once; your sister is dying." Sometimes, in the lab, telepathy works *too* well. Krippner cites a lab subject who sensed his experimenter's need for $25 to pay a bill.

People can and do pick up information on remote or hidden objects, persons or events: clairvoyance.

Under laboratory controls at Stanford Research Institute, scientists Harold Puthoff and Russell Targ studied the clairvoyant abilities of controversial Israeli Uri Geller. Seven times in a row, Geller accurately drew a picture hidden in two sealed opaque envelopes. Ten times without error, he identified which of ten identical sealed cans contained an object. The odds: one in a billion!

The Stanford Research Institute, now SRI International also verified clairvoyant abilities in six subjects with no previous psychic experience. All of them were able to describe in detail distant "target areas" picked by the scientists.

People can and do sense what is going to happen before it takes place: precognition.

In one of 15,000 validated cases compiled by Louisa Rhine, a 19-year-old California girl canceled plans to go to a funeral. She "had" to get to her mother. When she got home, her parents were calmly sitting in the living room. She "had" to get them out of their chairs. She claimed to be hungry and talked them into a snack in the kitchen. No sooner had they left the living room than a car crashed into the house, destroying the chairs in which the parents had been sitting.

So accurate have "hunches" of major events proved to be that a premonition registry has been set up in New York City. A few of the "hits" in registry files: the tragedy at Chappaquiddick, space-program failures and Martin Luther King's assassination.

People can and do move or affect objects, even distant ones, without touching them: psychokinesis.

After watching a film of the great Russian sensitive Nina Kulagina moving objects by gestures only or with her eyes, Felicia Parise of the staff of the Maimonides Dream Laboratory in Brooklyn performed some of the same feats under controlled conditions.

Bernard Grad, a biochemist at McGill University in Montreal, moistened seeds with water "treated" by a healer. Compared with those in a control group using ordinary water, "treated" seedlings grew faster, and the plants weighed more at the end of the strictly monitored experiment. Impressed with Grad's techniques and results, biophysicist M. Justa Smith, of the Human Dimensions Institute, Canandaigua, N.Y., demonstrated that an enzyme "treated" by the same healer showed significantly more activity than the "untreated."

WITH SO MUCH evidence now established concerning these four Psi or ESP phenomena, what about the scientific search for conditions under which they operate? Some discoveries so far:

1. Distance doesn't seem to matter. ESP has been recorded in the same room, and from outer space.

2. People who believe in ESP, or want it to work, usually do better at it.

3. People who feel close to each other appear to communicate better.

4. Shock events, such as accidents and disasters, come through—or at least are reported—much more often than neutral or happy ones.

5. ESP is more effective in altered states of consciousness such as deep relaxation, hypnosis and sleep. Most of the reported cases of precognition occur in dreams.

In some areas, there is less scientific consensus: Do psychic healers really heal? What about reincarnation? Is there such a thing as an "out-of-body" experience?

Psychologist Charles Tart, of the University of California at Davis, discovered a "Miss Z" for whom out-of-body experiences were so normal that when she was a child she thought everybody had them. In an elaborately prepared experiment, he arranged for her to sleep in a lab, with electrodes recording her brain waves, and "read" a randomly chosen five-digit number put on a shelf high over her head. While confined to her bed by the medical paraphernalia, she "floated up" and correctly identified the number.

The major dilemma in all such experiments is: *how* do you get scientific validation for Psi? The very tools and technology which would document psychic phenomena are based on the old premise that scientific fact is only what you can measure and observe. However, such metaphysical material by its nature resists capture, often going dead or turning off in a laboratory situation. Many people are instantly constrained when hitched up to a machine in a cubicle.

The noted psychic healer from Baltimore, Olga Worrall, recalls: "The first time I concentrated on a damaged leaf for a healing experiment [at U.C.L.A.], I 'burned it up.' I had to 'tone down' for the laboratory." Most of those who can work at all under laboratory conditions tend to taper off after a time—what scientists call the "decline effect."

Psychic Ingo Swann is a striking example of this scientific dilemma. Though he has been dramatically successful as a subject in rigidly controlled lab experiments—for instance, making temperature readings on instruments in insulated containers hotter or colder by force of will—indications are that such feats reveal only a portion of his psychic potential.

In out-of-body experiments—or remote viewing, as some researchers prefer to call it—Swann can "go" to any spot on the globe, given its latitude and longitude, and sketch correctly the mountains, rivers, roads and buildings just as they are at that point.

When asked in an experiment at the American Society for Psychical Research in New York to "go" to a hidden box and describe its contents, Swann rejoined, "You forgot to turn on the light in the box. It's dark." He was correct!

But these are minor accomplishments compared to what Swann and his colleagues seem able to do on their own. Once, filled with ennui by months of lab work in California, Swann phoned his friend, psychic Harold Sherman, 1500 miles away in Arkansas, and proposed they take a 600-million-mile trip together: "go" simultaneously to Jupiter, which neither of them knew anything about, but by which Pioneer 10 was scheduled to pass. Sherman agreed. Their respective observations of colors, landscapes, atmosphere and other conditions were filed the next day with astrophysicists and showed remarkable convergence. Nor were they far off from Pioneer 10 data.

Challenged by a science editor, they turned their attention to Mercury, by which Mariner 10 was soon to pass and radio back data. Prevailing opinion was that Mercury had neither atmosphere nor magnetic field. Yet each psychic reported a thin atmosphere and a magnetic field—confirmed by Mariner 10 within the month.

ON ONE THING numerous authorities agree: everyone has some degree of Psi. In not too many people, however, has the power begun to surface, and experts caution against trying to force it. California clinical psychologist Allan Y. Cohen points out, "There are at least 2000 documented cases of individuals needing psychological help, because of symptoms caused by prematurely and forcibly trying to develop psychic powers." Ernest Pecci, whose psychiatric specialty is "salvaging psychic casualties," warns against pushing into the unknown Psi jungle without guides and help. We must avoid phony gurus, drug-induced "trips," and take our cues from serious scientists. As Pascal Kaplan, parapsychology professor at John F. Kennedy University, in Orinda, Calif., notes: "What we now need is a kind of Psi Consumer Protection Agency, to inform and advise on things psychic."

We may not know exactly *what* Psi is, or exactly *how* it works, but we do know *that* it works. And as pragmatists we are already employing it:

• *In detective work*. A major retail chain in Toronto engaged a man with precognitive abilities to spot people about to shop-lift. He's correctly nabbed thousands—even predicting *what* they will take minutes before they do take it.

The late psychic Gerard Croiset of Utrecht, the Netherlands, was noted for unraveling many crimes. He picked up cues on the telephone. Once, called from a town some miles away to help locate a missing man, Croiset was able to say that the man had committed suicide by jumping off a bridge. His description of the locale was so accurate that police found the body by that afternoon.

• *In locating resources*. Clairvoyance is now being used to find water, minerals and archeological treasures. On play-by-play instructions from psychic Aron Abrahamsen, for instance, geologist-archeologist Jeffrey Goodman dug up deeply buried artifacts in Flagstaff, Ariz., which were over 100,000 years old—what could be the oldest clear-cut evidence of man in the Americas. Of Abrahamsen's 58 specific predictions tested so far in this case, 50 have proved correct. "ESP is replacing the spade as archeology's primary tool," says Goodman.

• *In health work*. Psychic healings may become commonplace someday. It is estimated that 70 percent of illnesses are brought on by stress and thinking oneself sick. "If you can think yourself sick, why not think yourself well?" asks osteopathic physician Irving Oyle. He is part of a growing network which practices "holistic" medicine, based on the power of consciousness to influence the body. "Treating disease through the mind is the coming thing in medicine," he declares. "But don't put me in the spook section. I'm just a family doctor turned medical researcher, trying to find out what it is that gets people well."

"One can become aware of the flow of energy within oneself and use it," says Jack Schwarz. He can control his bodily functions much as do the yogis in India. He can thrust an unsterilized knitting needle through his biceps, with no pain, bleeding or subsequent infection, the wound closing when the needle is withdrawn, and healing completely within a day or two. Schwarz's ability has been observed in the research department of the Menninger Foundation and elsewhere. A number of researchers believe that his self-healing ability can be learned. Schwarz devotes himself now to his own Aletheia Psychophysical Foundation in Oregon and teaches doctors and others "energy flow" techniques for preventing and healing disease.

BEYOND ALL THIS, Psi presents us with hints of a universal unity. Individual consciousness, it would appear, is part of a consciousness we all share. Each of us is part of everyone and everything in the universe. "Thou canst not stir a flower without troubling of a star," as visionary-poet Francis Thompson put it.

The deeper the psychic scientist probes, the closer he comes to the mystical religious vision. The Unity, the One, is the central concept and experience of all mysticism—Buddhist, Christian or Jewish, East or West.

And the more the physicist, traditional defender of materialist science, dissects physical reality, the closer he edges toward that same view. Quantum physicist Max Planck noted that it is impossible to obtain an adequate version of the laws we are seeking unless the physical system is regarded as a whole.

It was this Oneness that struck astronaut Edgar Mitchell on his trip to the moon, "merging the boundaries of the self with the cosmos." Then and there, Mitchell pledged his life and career to the understanding of consciousness, and what that could mean to the human condition. "We can't all go to the moon," he admits, "but perhaps the deeper awareness of Psi processes can provide the same perspective."

People were aghast when Copernicus proclaimed that the earth circles the sun. But the new view won out.

We may be at another such turning point today. In the words of Willis Harman of SRI International: "Psychic research in the next few decades may be destined to have an impact comparable to the impact a few centuries ago of Galileo and Copernicus. I call it the Second Copernican Revolution."

Could It Be
Coincidence?

A Curious Love Story

by Joseph P. Blank

AFTER THE prayers of the minister, the ring of relatives and friends around the twin graves broke up, and the mourners walked slowly away. It was difficult to believe that it was only two days earlier that Kurt and Helga had decided to drive to Erfurt in East Germany to buy black-currant plants for their garden. They had left their four-year-old daughter, Anna, with Kurt's younger brother, Martin. When their car blew a front tire and crashed into a concrete wall, the couple were killed instantly.

Beside the graves, Martin held the sobbing Anna in his arms. The child was frightened and unable to comprehend that she would never see her parents again. Martin stared at her delicate features, narrow face and tousled blond hair. She looked exactly like her mother at the age of four. Exactly. At that time, 26 years earlier, Martin had seen Helga only for a few minutes, but he vividly remembered that dazed, exhausted expression on her face. . . .

EARLY June was still chilly along the northeast coast of Germany, just south of Denmark. Kurt, 14, and Martin, 12, had permission from their mother to play along a favorite beach, but had been told, "Don't do more than wade, because the water is still too cold." Martin was the more spontaneous and outgoing of the brothers. Kurt was serious, thoughtful, almost taciturn. The one emotion that he expressed without reserve was a compassion for living things in trouble. He was always bringing home a stray dog or an injured bird.

As the boys came to the beach, they saw three young girls waving their arms toward the water and crying. They were the children of Heinz Meier, owner of the biggest farm in the area. Out at sea, bobbing on the swells, was a small yellow rubber boat. In it, barely visible, was four-year-old Helga Meier. The panic-stricken girls said that the dinghy had been pushed out to sea by the strong wind. Their nine-year-old brother had just left to find help.

Kurt said, "It's 45 minutes to the village. By the time help gets here, she'll be halfway to Denmark." He took off his shirt, trousers and shoes, and told Martin, "Keep the girls calm." He dashed through the surf and dived into the sea.

Martin had a watch, and now he clocked his brother. It took Kurt 32 minutes to reach the boat. Martin saw him alternately pushing then pulling it toward shore—opposed by a stiff wind. The rescue seemed to take forever. Finally, after an hour and 44 minutes, Kurt was close enough to shore to stand. Martin and the Meier girls splashed in to help. The oldest girl wrapped the frightened child in two sweaters and hurried from the beach. Help from the village had still not arrived.

Kurt collapsed face down on the sand. Martin rolled him over and rubbed him with a dry shirt. His skin was white, his lips were blue. After a few minutes, Kurt asked, "Where's the little girl?"

"They took her home. Are you all right?"

"I think so. I'll just lie here for a while."

On their slow walk home, Kurt told Martin of his ordeal. By the time he had reached the boat, Helga was in water up to her hips. He didn't climb into the boat for fear of sinking it. A cup attached to a light rope hung from the side; he untied it, then gave it to the child and told her to bail. Clutching the rope, Kurt tried to swim, but made little progress against the rough waves. He put the rope between his teeth and swam backward. When he tired, he swung behind the boat, held on, and kicked hard until he felt able to use his arms again for swimming.

All the while Kurt thought that he and the child would surely drown. But somewhere he found the strength to reach shore.

News of the heroic rescue spread through the village. As congratulations poured in, however, Kurt appeared more and more disconsolate. "He never said a word," recalls his older sister, Iris. "But I knew what was wrong. Old man Meier didn't thank him for saving his daughter. Helga's mother would have, but she was dying in a sanitarium.

"Meier was a hard man, and he never once gave a sign that he even knew Kurt existed. After about a week, Kurt seemed to get over his disappointment. He never again mentioned the rescue."

WORLD War II was now at its height, and Kurt's family moved from their coastal village to Weimar, in the interior of Germany.

The years passed. Iris married. Martin married, too, and had two boys. Kurt became a schoolteacher and remained single. (Martin used to call him *Hagestolz,* or "confirmed bachelor.") He rarely dated or went dancing. His recreation was chess, and he became a top player in the coffeehouses of Weimar. He had a dry sense of humor and an almost cynical attitude, which Iris thought was a disguise to hide his sensitivity.

In 1962—20 years to the summer after the rescue of Helga—Kurt's ailing mother decided to visit relatives in her old home village in what had now become West Germany. Because she was sick and over 65, the East German government granted Kurt a three-day pass to accompany her.

On his second day in the village, Kurt took a walk to the beach where he had rescued Helga. Sitting on a rock staring out to sea, he suddenly realized that he wasn't alone. A tanned, blond young woman with a slim, almost boyish figure was leaning against a nearby tree.

Quite uncharacteristically, Kurt walked over to her. Impulsively, he told her that he had grown up in the village and that this was his first visit in 20 years. They began walking along the beach, shoes in hand. "Look," Kurt said, "my mother is visiting relatives, and I'm bored. Let's go dancing tonight."

She smiled. "Why not?" she replied, almost aggressively. "My name is Helga Meier."

Kurt stopped short. "The little girl in the yellow boat! Twenty years ago. Do you remember? I'm Kurt."

Helga nodded. "I heard that you were in town. I've come down to the beach three times hoping that you would be here. I wanted to thank you." Her expression turned somber. "Don't call for me at the house. I'll meet you at the crossroads."

That evening, Kurt and Helga did no dancing. They talked. Helga was depressed. "I always wanted to thank you," she said. "But I've often wondered whether it might have been better if you hadn't rescued me that morning. I think Meier feels the same way. He believes that my mother was unfaithful. I don't look like his other children, and he has never behaved as if he were my father.

"The rest of the family have followed his lead and treat me like a servant. I do housework and farmwork. I get nothing for it, and Meier keeps telling me that I am illegitimate. I have no one."

Seething inside Kurt was a feeling that he had never before experienced. Holding her hands, he leaned toward Helga and kissed her. "I must leave tomorrow," he told her. "Come with me. Marry me."

She was startled. "But you've known me for only a few hours."

"I know you. I love you."

Then, in a low voice, Helga said, "I like you very much. I think I could love you, but I don't really know." She smiled at Kurt. "Yes, I will go with you. I risk nothing. It is you who are taking the risk."

The next morning, Kurt confronted Meier outside the front door of his big house. He introduced himself—the name rang no bell with Meier—and flatly told the glowering farmer that he was taking Helga to Weimar to marry her.

The news infuriated Meier, but Kurt was adamant. "You can't stop me. It's difficult to get a pass out of East Germany. I am taking Helga with me now."

BACK in Weimar, an astonished Martin couldn't believe that Kurt—his quiet, cautious bachelor brother—had met, proposed to and actually carried off a young woman within 24 hours. "And what's even more unbelievable," Martin told his wife, "is that it's *this* girl."

Love was magic for Kurt. His reserve was replaced by spontaneity. He laughed freely. His sense of humor turned from the sardonic to the gentle.

Helga was slower to change. During the first few months she was shy, withdrawn.

Gradually, however, her fears and doubts evaporated. She smiled more—a slow, understanding smile that turned her from pretty to beautiful. The explanation for her change was simple: she had fallen in love with her husband. In two years Helga gave birth to Anna. Kurt was unabashedly proud of his wife and daughter.

The couple were rarely apart. Kurt stopped visiting the coffeehouses where the best chess players gathered; he didn't want to take time from his wife and daughter. He had always disliked working with soil, but when Helga decided to plant a large plot of land, he became an avid gardener and worked at her side. Amazed, Martin told his wife, "I've never seen love change a man so much."

Their love continued to grow. Martin could see it in the way they communicated with a mere touch or glance. Even on social occasions they always sat together. Kurt couldn't keep his eyes off his wife, and Martin once kidded him about it. "I like to watch her," Kurt admitted. "She moves so beautifully, so gracefully."

"Good Lord, you really are in love with your wife," Martin laughed.

Kurt gave his brother a big grin and said, "Forever."

MARTIN now recalls, "Those were Kurt's best years. And they were the happiest and merriest years for all of us. When Kurt and Helga left, they took a lot of that happiness and merriment with them."

One beautiful summer Sunday, a year before the accident, the two families were in the garden that Helga and Kurt had made. The wives were picking berries; the children were playing; Kurt and Martin sat in the shade of an old, twisted pine tree, relaxed and at peace. Kurt began talking: "You know, before Helga, I really wasn't dissatisfied with my life. I knew what I had, and that was fine with me. But I didn't know what I didn't have.

"Then, Helga! She opened a new world for me. Maybe I did the same for her. She made me know what being alive is, what it means. Now I can't imagine myself without her."

He paused, then said, "Do you believe that some things in life are destined to be? Is it possible? Was it meant for me to save her 25 years ago—for myself?"

"Tell Us About Fichtenhorst!"

by Hans Hardt

IT WAS a chill September evening in 1951. As I stepped off the westbound train at the last village in the Soviet Zone of East Germany, I cast a grateful glance at the dark clouds overhead. It was just the right weather to slip back across the border into West Germany unnoticed.

I sought out a dimly lit café. There, nursing a glass of lemonade while I waited for night to close in, I relived the few days I had just spent with my parents and brother—our first family reunion in over seven years. It had been saddened by my parents' destitution. They had lost all their belongings when they fled from the onrushing Soviet armies in 1945, only to be overrun by the Red tide in the town where they were now living. Return to our native village of Fichtenhorst was both unthinkable and forbidden: it now belonged to satellite Poland.

I had been living in West Germany since my release from a prisoner-of-war camp in Britain, in 1948. Finally able to trace my parents' whereabouts, I learned that my father, long an invalid, was now crippled with multiple sclerosis, and I determined to get him to West Germany for proper medical treatment. But, after months of waiting, my application for a Soviet visa had been turned down "on political grounds"—presumably because as a POW I had spent four years in England.

In May 1951 I had tried to slip into East Germany to see my parents, only to be stopped at the frontier and turned back with my passport stamped "Illegal Crossing of the Border."

Now, four months later, I had tried again and had gotten through. I knew that to be caught a second time, trying to get out after several days' unreported sojourn in the Soviet Zone, would mean something worse than a stamp on my passport.

I was fairly hopeful of getting back into West Germany, however, because of the detailed map my brother had drawn for me. It plotted precisely the camouflaged positions of border guards, noted the hours when some posts were unmanned, and indicated various landmarks such as the high chimneys of several factories near the border.

My watch showed 11. It was time to go.

For two hours I walked a deserted country road. When a hamlet came into view I turned sharp right, and minutes later entered the forest that stretched across the frontier. I crouched down and struck a match for a last look at my map, stuffed the paper into my pocket, and resumed walking. Every few minutes I stood still and listened, to be sure that the rustling sounds were merely wind and leaves. Soon I was close to the path dividing East from West. And then:

"Stoi!" a voice shouted in Russian. "Stop!"

I threw myself on the ground, rolled a few yards, staggered to my feet and ran. A tommygun chattered, and two white flares plopped overhead. When the shooting stopped, I heard the terrifying noise of dogs in full cry. Something hit my back and knocked me headlong into a clump of bushes. When I lifted my head I was looking into the panting jaws of a German Shepherd dog.

Two Russian soldiers yanked me to my feet. While one of them held the warm barrel of his tommygun under my chin, the other emptied my pockets. They bound my hands and marched me through the forest. Suddenly my blood froze—I remembered the map!

That night I paced a cold cellar room with barred windows, berating myself for not having destroyed that piece of paper. To the Russians, I felt sure, it would be conclusive proof that I was a spy.

Early next morning two guards hustled me to a little office upstairs. Behind a big black desk sat an officer in a major's uniform, with the hated red tabs on the collar of his jacket betokening a member of the Soviet security police.

"Good morning, *kleiner Spion*," he said, with cold sarcasm. "Did you sleep well?"

I was startled to be addressed in good German, although I knew that the Soviet forces had been combed for men fluent in the language for service in East Germany. But the major's tactics were Russian enough: the contempt in the phrase *kleiner Spion* (little spy); the assumption of guilt; the apparent expectation that I would make a clean breast of things quickly.

"I am not a spy," I protested.

"I didn't ask your profession, *kleiner Spion*, but how you slept. So you crossed the border illegally four months ago! Tell me, what did you try to find out this time?"

"Nothing. I went only to see my parents."

"And where do they live?"

"I won't tell."

"We have ways of finding out," the major said.

He was looking through my passport. "So you were born in Fichtenhorst?" He looked at me sharply for a moment, closed my passport, then picked up the hand-drawn map.

"Fine drawing, that. Roads, villages, our guard positions, even the location of some large factories. How much do the Americans give you for such a nice drawing?"

I was silent. I realized how feeble my explanation would sound.

"All right, little spy," he snapped. "Maybe you will talk in Siberia! Guards, take him away."

Cold fear gripped me at the dread word, "Siberia." But dead tired, hungry, I was no sooner in my cell than I dozed off despite my fears. I could not tell how long I had slept when the guards woke me and led me before the major again. He lit a cigarette and studied me through the smoke.

"We have checked the information on your passport. All lies. Now we know you are a spy. You had better talk."

I stood dumbfounded. "I have no reason to lie to you," I protested.

"We'll see about that. How long did you live in Fichtenhorst, little spy?"

"For the first 13 years of my life."

"All right, tell us about Fichtenhorst. We happen to know that village." He closed his eyes and leaned back in his chair, ready to listen.

I spoke of our village east of the river Oder, of the old church amid the lime trees. I told how we farm boys washed the horses at the river bank in the evening. I mentioned the village priest, the local schoolteacher's foibles, my own grandmother who owned a big farm and was loved for her good deeds.

Through it all the major's face remained a wooden mask. When I stopped, he opened his eyes and asked, "Then you knew Wolfgang Leuters, Magda Furst and Walter Korb, for example?"

I wondered what devil's game he was playing. I remembered no such people in the village in my time.

"Or the farmer Stolpel—Ignaz Stolpel?" he continued.

"Yes, yes, that one I knew. Did you know him, major?"

"Shut up!" His voice rasped. "I ask the questions here. Tell me what you know about this Stolpel."

"Well, he was the poorest farmer in Fichtenhorst. His land was so bad that even the weeds were scrawny. Everybody felt sorry for him, because he worked hard. He never complained, though, and he was too proud to accept help. Frau Stolpel worked on the land every day, too, and Josef—that was his son. His father drove the boy as hard as he drove himself. Nobody thought that unjust. It was the lot of most boys in the village. When he was 16, Josef left home. It was said he had gone south to Czechoslovakia, but nobody knew for sure."

I paused, remembering the pity we had all felt for the Stolpels. "Go on!" the major ordered.

I told how the poor farmer had changed after losing his son. He turned against the village, refusing even to come to Mass and forbidding his wife to go. People said that on Sundays, when the bells rang out, she would cry her heart out, for she was very devout.

"Why wouldn't he let her go?" the major asked.

"They said she sided with the boy, and Stolpel was bitter about it. He didn't want her to talk with people. Two years after her son ran away, Frau Stolpel died. Her husband came to the funeral in his working clothes. Then he went back to his fields and worked long into the night. He became more silent and hostile than ever."

I paused. "Do you want me to go on, major?"

"Yes."

My grandmother, I told him, wanted to help the lonely man. She offered him good land in exchange for his barren fields, but he shook his head and went on working. Then one day he was found face down on the ground. He was rushed to the hospital in a nearby town. He had had a stroke. His farm was auctioned off, but that didn't bring enough money even to pay the hospital.

"In the spring he came back," I went on. "My grandmother found him wandering on his old farm and led him to our house. She gave him a room, and he sat at our table. He rarely spoke, even in thanks, but he did everything he could to earn his food.

"To my boyish eyes he seemed very old, with his white hair and tottering step. At first I was a little afraid of him. Then one day when I was trying to make my first fishing rod and bungling the job, he took it from me, finished it skillfully and gave it back. He did all this without speaking, but with a gentleness that took away my fear. After that there was between us an unspoken friendship.

"When he died, Grandmother found his wife's prayer book sewn inside his mattress. In it was a scribbled note: 'Father, I go away now and will never come back. I go away because you do not love me. Please be good to Mother.' It was signed 'Josef.'

"Now do you believe I am from Fichtenhorst?" I finished, a bit embarrassed because I had let myself ramble on about an old man and his sorrow.

The major did not answer. "Go back to your cell!" he ordered harshly. As I turned to leave, he picked up the map. With dismay I realized that he had given me no chance to explain away that incriminating paper—and people had drawn sentences of five and ten years at hard labor on flimsier evidence of spying. I had fallen into his trap. The fact that he had not once mentioned the map was proof to me that his mind was made up.

I slept through the night, stupefied by fatigue and hopelessness. Early in the morning a guard woke me.

"Get ready!"

This was it. I was numb with despair.

"We will take you to the Western Zone," the guard said.

Throughout the hour's walk to the border between two soldiers I kept expecting to be turned back. This was some cruel trick, I was sure. And I still only half believed when they handed me my papers and motioned for me to cross the line into West Germany.

"You are lucky," one of them said, not unkindly.

How right he was I understood only when I looked into my passport and saw there a new stamp: "Second Illegal Crossing of the Border." It was signed: Major Josef Stolpel.

It Happened
on the Brooklyn Subway

by Paul Deutschman

THERE ARE two different explanations of what happened as the
result of a subway ride taken by Hungarian-born Marcel Sternberger on the afternoon of January 10, 1948.

Some people will say that Sternberger's sudden impulse to
visit a sick friend in Brooklyn—and the bright world of dramatic events that followed—was part of a string of lucky coincidences. Others will see the guiding hand of Divine Providence in everything that happened that day.

But whatever the explanation, here are the facts:

STERNBERGER, a New York portrait photographer living in
a Long Island suburb, has followed for years an unchanging
routine in going from his home to his office on Fifth Avenue.
A methodical man of nearly 50, with bushy white hair, guileless
brown eyes and the bouncing enthusiasm of a *czardas* dancer
of his native Hungary, Sternberger always takes the 9:09 Long
Island Railroad train to Woodside, at which station he catches
a subway train to the city.

On the morning of January 10, he boarded the 9:09 as usual.
En route he suddenly decided to visit Laszlo Victor, a Hungarian friend who lived in Brooklyn and who was ill.

"I don't know why I decided to go to see him that morning,"
Sternberger told me some weeks afterward. "I could have done

it after office hours. But I kept thinking that he could stand a little cheering up."

Accordingly, at Ozone Park Sternberger changed to the subway for Brooklyn, went to his friend's house and stayed until midafternoon. He then boarded a Manhattan-bound subway for his office.

"The car was crowded," Sternberger told me, "and there seemed to be no chance of a seat. But just as I entered, a man sitting by the door suddenly jumped up to leave and I slipped into the empty place.

"I've been living in New York long enough not to be in the habit of starting conversations with strangers. But, being a photographer, I have the peculiar habit of analyzing people's faces, and I was struck by the features of the passenger on my left. He was probably in his late 30s and his eyes seemed to have a hurt expression in them. He was reading a Hungarian-language newspaper and something prompted me to turn to him and say in Hungarian, 'I hope you don't mind if I glance at your paper.'

"The man seemed surprised to be addressed in his native language but he answered politely, 'You may read it now. I'll have time later on.'

"During the half-hour ride to town we had quite a conversation. He said his name was Paskin. A law student when the war started, he had been put into a labor battalion and sent to the Ukraine. Later he was captured by the Russians and put to work burying the German dead. After the war he had covered hundreds of miles on foot, until he reached his home in Debrecen, a large city in eastern Hungary.

"I myself knew Debrecen quite well, and we talked about it for a while. Then he told me the rest of his story. When he went to the apartment once occupied by his father, mother, brothers and sisters, he found strangers living there. Then he went upstairs to the apartment he and his wife had once had. It also was occupied by strangers. None of them had ever heard of his family.

"As he was leaving, full of sadness, a boy ran after him, calling: '*Paskin bacsi! Paskin bacsi!*' That means 'Uncle Paskin.' The child was the son of some old neighbors of his. He went to the boy's home and talked to his parents. 'Your whole family is dead,' they told him. 'The Nazis took them and your wife to Auschwitz.'

"Auschwitz was one of the worst concentration camps. Paskin thought of the Nazi gas chambers, and gave up all hope. A few days later, too heartsick to remain longer in Hungary, which to him was a funeral land, he set out again on foot, stealing across border after border until he reached Paris. He had managed to emigrate to the United States in October 1947, just three months before I met him.

"All the time he had been talking, I kept thinking that somehow his story seemed familiar. Suddenly I knew why. A young woman whom I had met recently at the home of friends had also been from Debrecen; she had been sent to Auschwitz; from there she had been transferred to work in a German munitions factory. Her relatives had been killed in the gas chambers. Later, she was liberated by the Americans and was brought here in the first boatload of Displaced Persons in 1946. Her story had moved me so much that I had written down her address and phone number, intending to invite her to meet my family and thus help relieve the terrible emptiness in her present life.

"It seemed impossible that there could be any connection between these two people, but when I reached my station I stayed on the train and asked in what I hoped was a casual voice, 'Is your first name Bela?'

"He turned pale. 'Yes!' he answered. 'How did you know?'

"I fumbled anxiously in my address book. 'Was your wife's name Marya?'

"He looked as if he were about to faint. 'Yes! Yes!' he said.

"I said, 'Let's get off the train.' I took him by the arm at the next station and led him to a phone booth. He stood there like a man in a trance while I searched for the number in my address book. It seemed hours before I had the woman called Marya Paskin on the other end. (Later, I learned her room was alongside the telephone but she was in the habit of never answering it because she had so few friends and the calls were always for someone else. This time, however, there was no one else at home and, after letting it ring for a while, she answered it.)

"When I heard her voice, at last, I told her who I was and asked her to describe her husband. She seemed surprised at the question but gave me a description. Then I asked her where she had lived in Debrecen and she told me the address.

"Asking her to hold the wire, I turned to Paskin and said,

'Did you and your wife live on such-and-such a street?'

"'Yes!' Bela exclaimed. He was white as a sheet, and trembling.

"'Try to be calm,' I urged him. 'Something miraculous is about to happen to you. Here, take this telephone and talk to your wife!'

"He nodded his head in mute bewilderment, his eyes bright with tears. He took the receiver, listened a moment to his wife's voice, then suddenly cried, 'This is Bela! This is Bela!' and began to mumble hysterically. Seeing that the poor fellow was so excited he couldn't talk coherently, I took the receiver from his shaking hands.

"I began talking to Marya, who also sounded hysterical. 'Stay where you are,' I told her. 'I am sending your husband to you. He will be there in a few minutes.'

"Bela was crying like a baby and saying over and over again, 'It is my wife. I go to my wife!'

"At first I thought I had better accompany Paskin lest the man should faint from excitement, but decided that this was a moment in which no stranger should intrude. Putting Paskin into a taxicab, I directed the driver to take him to Marya's address, paid the fare and said good-by."

Bela Paskin's reunion with his wife was a moment so poignant, so electric with suddenly released emotion, that afterward neither he nor Marya could recall anything about it.

"I remember only that when I left the phone I walked to the mirror like in a dream to see maybe if my hair had turned gray," she said later. "The next thing I know a taxi stops in front of the house and it is my husband who comes toward me. Details I cannot remember; only this I know—that I was happy for the first time in many years.

"Even now it is difficult to believe that it happened. We have both suffered so much; I have almost lost the capability to be not afraid. Each time my husband goes from the house I say to myself, 'Will anything happen to take him from me again?'"

Her husband is confident that no overwhelming misfortune will ever again befall them. "Providence has brought us together," he says simply. "It was meant to be."

Skeptical persons would no doubt attribute the events of that memorable afternoon to mere chance. But was it chance that made Sternberger suddenly decide to visit his sick friend, and hence take a subway line that he had never been on before? Was it chance that caused the man sitting by the door of the car to rush out just as Sternberger came in? Was it chance that caused Bela Paskin to be sitting beside Sternberger, reading a Hungarian newspaper?

Was it chance—or did God ride the Brooklyn subway that afternoon?

Triplets...
And They Didn't Know It!

by Phyllis Battelle

ALL HIS LIFE, 19-year-old Robert Shafran sensed he was special. He had no idea why he felt this way, although he knew he had a near-genius I.Q. of 148, and recognized that he was an irrepressible extrovert. Adults sometimes sighed, "Bobby, when they made you, they broke the mold." Bobby rather liked that; it appealed to his quirky sense of humor and strong sense of individuality. Yet he had a recurring dream "about a kid who looked like me, talked like me and acted like me." When he woke from it, his feelings of being special were strongly reinforced.

As a teen-ager, Bobby saw psychiatrists in an attempt to discover why his school performance was falling short of his obvious potential. Their conclusion: it had something to do with his having been adopted an an infant. He dismissed that theory, knowing that his adoptive parents, a Scarsdale, N.Y., physician and his attorney wife, "gave me all the love and support I could ever want." And indeed they did.

"Bobby didn't say a word until he was four," says Elsa Shafran, now retired. "But when he began to speak, it was in long and articulate sentences." Dr. Morton Shafran adds fondly, "He was always precocious, but also restless and hyperkinetic." These qualities set him somewhat apart from the world, as though something was missing inside him. Last autumn, Bobby discovered what it was.

On September 3, Bobby enrolled as a freshman at Sullivan County Community College in upstate New York. After he had checked in to his dormitory, he began circulating on campus. "I'm gregarious," he explains, "and I was saying 'Hello, how are you?' to everyone in sight."

Suddenly some students were slapping his back: "Hey, Eddy, how you doin'?"

Bobby grinned. "Fine, guys. But I'm not Eddy."

"Sure you're not—you joker."

Next day the phenomenon continued. "It got increasingly fascinating. Girls were hugging me and calling me Eddy," he recalls. He showed them his driver's license, proving he was Robert Shafran, but that left them unconvinced. One even told him where a birthmark was located on his body—an intimate spot. He was stunned.

The second night, a student named Michael Domnitz walked into his room asking, "Is this 11-C?"

"Yeah."

"Are you—" and at that point Bobby turned around and saw his visitor's face go totally white. "He just stared at me, freaked out. Then he asked, 'Were you adopted?' When I nodded, he asked when I was born, and I told him July 12, 1961. 'Where?' Long Island Jewish-Hillside Medical Center. He grabbed my arm and said, 'Come with me. I've got to show you some pictures!'"

They rushed to another dorm where Domnitz pulled out a snapshot of his best friend, Eddy Galland, who had attended the school the year before, then transferred to another community college near his home in New Hyde Park, N.Y., on Long Island. Now it was Bobby's turn to freak out. "What I saw was a photograph of myself," he says in a hushed voice. "It was like looking in a mirror. It was unmistakably *me*. I didn't know what to say or do."

Mike Domnitz picked up the phone and began dialing.

Eddy Galland remembers wondering, when the phone rang at 9 p.m., whether it was another weird call from acquaintances upstate "who had been spending their allowances all day to tell me, 'Hey, there's somebody here who looks exactly like you.' Then Mike put Bobby on the phone. Bobby said 'Eddy, I think you're my twin brother.' I said very calmly, 'Yeah?' Then he said, 'Listen, I've got the same eyes, same nose, same hair, and we were born at the same hospital on the same day.'"

The two made arrangements to meet that weekend. But then Bobby decided he couldn't wait. "I told Mike, 'I've got to see Eddy *tonight!*' And we both got in my car and drove three hours to the Galland home."

At 2 a.m. they knocked on Eddy's door. "It seemed forever," Bobby recalls, "before the door opened. After that, I said, 'Oh, my God'—and simultaneously *saw* myself saying, 'Oh, my God.' I scratched my head—and saw myself scratching my head. I turned away, and saw myself turning away. Everything in unison, as though professional mimes were doing this. We started shaking hands, and wound up hugging."

In the words of both young men, there was "an instantaneous feeling of love."

That early morning, in the Galland living room, the two brothers quickly noticed other similarities. Both smoked the same brand of cigarettes. Both liked Italian food and mellow rock music. But the first, brief meeting was relatively superficial. "We could hardly talk," Eddy says, "and my dad kept taking pictures. My parents couldn't believe it."

After an hour Bobby and Mike drove back to school. Later that morning Bobby phoned his home and cried, "Dad, Dad, I just met my twin brother!"

Dr. Shafran replied logically, "Bobby, an adoption agency doesn't separate twins." Neither set of parents had been informed that their sons were multiple-birth babies.

That Sunday Bobby and Eddy met again on Long Island and took turns recounting their life experiences. Both had a high I.Q., yet each had had problems in school at the same time. They'd each had psychiatric therapy in 1977 and 1978, and been told their problems were rooted in their adoption; both called that "baloney." They were similarly attracted to older girls—and had serious relationships with women of 27. Their best sport was wrestling, and they had the same favorite moves and fastest pinning time: 18 seconds. "I discovered that whenever I'd had troubles, Eddy had had troubles," Bobby says. "When I had excelled, he'd excelled. It was overwhelming."

That was only the beginning. The Long Island newspaper *Newsday* heard of the startling reunion about two weeks after it happened and interviewed the twins. The story was picked up by the New York *Post* and the New York *Daily News*.

On the day the article appeared in the *Post,* David Kellman, a 19-year-old college student from Queens, N.Y., saw the picture of Bobby and Eddy. His pulse rate doubled.

"These two people were my mirror image," he says. "But the story didn't give a date of birth, so I tried to keep my emotions low-key and inside till I was sure." That night at home, David hesitantly held out the *Post* and said, "Ma, check this out." Claire Kellman tossed her son a copy of the *Daily News*—which carried no picture but gave a date of birth—and said, "Check *this* out."

"Right then we knew," David says. "We looked up the phone number of the Galland house. Eddy was out, but his mother answered. I said, 'You're not going to believe this, Mrs. Galland, but my name is David Kellman, and I think I'm the third. . . .'"

That evening David and his parents drove over to the Galland home. Eddy watched as the Kellman car parked beside the curb and "still another me climbed out and started up the walk. I opened the door a little, then closed it. I opened it again, saw his face, and closed it again. It was like a double take, a triple take—and the third time I opened it David was saying, in a voice just like my own, 'I haven't seen you in 19 years—don't slam the door in my face!'"

Slowly, they moved toward each other. "I can't *believe* this!" they said simultaneously. Then, again in unison, "I can't believe you *said* that!"—and fell into each other's arms.

David pulled out his cigarettes—the same brand Bobby and Eddy smoked. Like his brothers, David had flunked math despite a high I.Q., gone through psychiatric care, enjoyed Italian food, wrestling, older women ("not in that order"), and had dreamed he had a brother who looked like him.

David felt "euphoria," and Eddy thoroughly enjoyed the night. "We just kept talking and saying, 'Wow, did you do that too?'"

It was probably the first time in history that identical triplets separated in infancy have been reunited. Each child was brought up in a somewhat different environment by working parents. The Shafrans are medical and legal professionals; Richard and Claire Kellman operate a wholesale housewares business; Elliott Galland is an industrial-arts teacher and his wife, Annette, is an executive secretary.

Predictably, scientists have now flooded the families with requests to study the triplets. But the 19-year-olds are too consumed with their joyful, sometimes zany, self-discovery to hold still for inquiry. "We have never been genuinely, intrinsically happy like this before," explains David. "Give us a chance."

The families' first priority was to contact the adoption agency and inquire why the boys had been separated. None of the parents was pleased with the explanation that, 19 years ago, little was known of the potentially harmful effects of splitting up multiple-birth children. The triplets were said to be the last such infants separated.

No one can be certain whether they would have led less complex emotional lives if they had stayed together, but the presumption is strong. "We all had periods of being miserable, a lot of emotional pain, in spite of having terrific parents," says Bobby. "Psychiatrists told each of us there was some kind of emotional block."

It is a rare, serious moment in an interview with Bobby, David and Eddy. Their eccentric sense of humor seems to combine the drollery of the early Beatles and the horseplay of the Marx Brothers. They often yelp with laughter, then switch gears to calm, straight-faced conversation that invariably ends in one triplet finishing another's sentence. They confess they can be "really wild sometimes" when together, but they're trying, gradually, to settle down.

David intends to become a businessman. Bobby, whose mother says he has been cooking since the age of four, plans to operate hotels and restaurants. Eddy will be a doctor. They phone or see one another several times a day and meet often at one another's homes.

"They're all so happy," says Dr. Shafran with a smile. "But they're rushing to make up for 19 years of being apart. They get kind of fractious. I only hope they won't let all this distract them from their education and goals. You can't make a career out of being a triplet."

In spite of the wonder of finding "our own flesh and blood," the triplets say they have no interest in locating their biological parents. "There may be an underlying curiosity, but it isn't relevant," Eddy says.

Bobby adds, "A woman gave birth to us. We appreciate that. She made sure we got into good homes, and we appreciate that. But we all have intelligent parents who cared for us, went through trials and heartaches with us. They are our real parents."

All three of the triplets agree with that.

The Amazing End of Flight 193

by Allen Rankin

As THE Boeing 727 lifted from the runway and the lights of Mobile vanished below, passenger Cheryl Saiter, 33, glanced nervously at her watch. It was 9:04 p.m. Just 18 more minutes and National Airlines Flight 193 would be safely on the ground at Pensacola; she and her surgeon-husband Joe, sitting beside her in the coach section, would be home. Or so Cheryl tried to reassure herself.

Even before leaving the Bahamas that afternoon she had had a premonition about flying today—May 8, 1978. Now, boring through the black night in the third plane of the trip, she was nearly frantic with foreboding. She even felt it ominous that she had happened to take a seat by the emergency exit over the plane's left wing.

She was acting like a frightened child, Cheryl decided, mainly because this was May. She and Joe had had some bad scares in May: the premature birth of their youngest child, Judd, and the near-drowning of their daughter Sherie. Cheryl had concluded, only half jokingly, that the Saiters were "jinxed in May."

She forced herself to think of pleasant things: of her three children waiting at home in the little village of Gulf Breeze on Pensacola Bay; of puttering around in the family launch and fishing in the choice waters in front of their neighbor Glenn McDonald's cottage.

89

9:10. In Escambia Bay east of Pensacola, lean, tough Glenn McDonald, 41, stood on the bridge of his tugboat *Little Mac* and squinted through the fog at the crane-equipped barge he was pushing. He, too, wished he were at home. Ordinarily, he would have been there hours ago—but late that afternoon his marine salvage and construction company had received an emergency call to repair the jammed swing-bridge of a railroad trestle at the head of the bay. He and his mate, Bill Kenney, planned to make a quick trip of the 25 miles to the trestle, then get a good night's sleep before starting work at sunup. But now pea-soup fog was rolling in so thick they had lost the channel markers, and McDonald had slowed to a creeping two knots. "Where are we?" McDonald muttered to himself. "And what are we doing out here anyway?"

9:16. Cheryl Saiter peered anxiously through her window. At this stage of the flight she could usually see the lights of Pensacola; but now there was just blackness. Joe sensed her rising tension and gave her an affectionate pat.

9:17. In the cockpit, Capt. George T. Kunz, 55, was gradually bringing the plane down. The overcast above Pensacola airport was getting critically low, and the tower had reminded Kunz that the airport's instrument-landing system, whose electronic beam could have guided him in through almost any weather, was out of service.

So Captain Kunz was making a surveillance approach. If he couldn't see the runway lights clearly at the allowed minimum descent altitude of 480 feet, he would return to Mobile. The final decision would be up to him. And Kunz's record of making right decisions was perfect. In 32 years of flying he had never put a scratch on an airplane.

9:20:12. "Three and a half miles from the runway and on course," reported the air traffic controller. The 727's three flight officers were busy with the ritual of descent: reducing speed, setting flaps, lowering the landing gear.

9:20:15. At about 500 feet, the airliner's ground-proximity warning system went off with its startling *whoop-whooping* sound, flashing red lights on the panel, and a recorded voice insisting "Pull up! Pull up!" But Captain Kunz, as he would later testify at a hearing, was beginning to misread his altimeter. He believed the plane to be 1000 feet higher than it actually was. He was sure the altimeter read 1500 feet, not 500. Both he and co-pilot Leonard G. Sanderson, Jr., 31, concluded the alarm was screaming because they were descending at an excess rate—another hazard that could activate the warning system.

When flight engineer James K. Stockwell switched off the alarm and its confusing din, Kunz assumed that the alarm had shut off because he had reduced his rate of descent. The big airliner continued to sweep downward to 400, 200. Senior flight attendant Carol Crawford, 29, stood near the forward boarding door, ready to make the final landing announcement.

9:20:31. Co-pilot Sanderson was double-checking Kunz in the reading of the altimeter. But he too had misread the instrument. Suddenly realizing the error, Sanderson said, "Hey, hey, we're down to 50 feet!" Too late. With a thunderous boom, the plane was down.

Wrenched violently against her seat belt, Cheryl Saiter heard an ear-splitting series of bangs. The cabin lights went out and she felt an icy fluid dash over her head and sting her eyes. Jet fuel, she realized, and thought with terror and wonder, *Now we will explode . . . fly apart . . . burn . . .*

But the 66-ton airliner had made a remarkably fortunate contact with the planet. It had come down in the unobstructed waters of Escambia Bay. And it had hit the water at a nose-up angle, converting a crash into a belly-flop landing.

Abruptly, the motion and the racket ceased, and the dim auxiliary lights came on. Cheryl heard Joe say calmly, "Come on, let's get out of here." He leaned across her and jerked open the emergency door. Seeing waves lapping over the wing, they paused to dig life jackets from beneath their seats, then stepped out into darkness and the cold bay.

Water was rising fast in the plane, especially in the rear cabin. Flight attendant Crawford seized a megaphone and shouted, "Get your life vests from under your seats and come forward!" In waist-deep water, she began herding passengers toward the right, front galley door. Passengers opened other doors. In the scramble, there were cries and screams, but little real panic.

Within minutes, almost everybody was off the plane and into the bay's choppy two-foot waves. Some wore life jackets, some did not. Many of the survivors were hurt or in shock. Some clung to parts of the sinking plane, others clung to them. How long could they hold out?

But—incredibly—help was close at hand. In the strangest

of fate's quirks that night, the 727 had landed practically on top of the only boat operating in that part of the bay—Glenn McDonald's also-lost-in-the-fog *Little Mac*. Moments before, McDonald and Kenney had looked up amazed as the airliner, landing lights ablaze, shrieked down out of the murk from astern, and plowed into the bay about 200 yards off their port beam. And both men, feeling an electric jolt go up their spines, *knew* why they were here off course in this unlikely spot, at this unlikely hour.

McDonald pinned the tug's spotlight on the airliner and swung the barge hard to port. He shoved the throttle to full speed—all the six knots his old diesel would do. Kenney ran back to the tug's radio and got off some "Mayday" calls. Then he readied all the boat's life preservers and tied ropes to the barge cleats to serve as boarding lines.

The 30-by-70-foot barge, nudged along by a 30-foot, single-screw tug—in all, 200 unwieldy tons of steel—was hardly the ideal rescue craft. With one slip of the wheel or throttle McDonald feared he would crush the plane like an eggshell or kill people in the water. The stench of jet fuel warned him that a spark from his engine might blow up everybody on the scene.

But there was no time for hesitation. Approaching the plane on its left side, he could see it was already more than half submerged. People were standing in its flooded doors; others scrambled for footing on its cabin top or bobbed in the waves around it, shouting for help. McDonald edged the barge within several yards of a cluster of swimmers and stopped.

"Swim this way and grab a rope!" Kenney shouted from the barge. No ordinary seaman, 28-year-old Bill Kenney was precisely the right man for this job. A stockily built man of extraordinary strength and endurance, he had been a commercial diver and medical technician on the Great Lakes, and a Marine demolition diver in Vietnam. Wrapping his legs around a cleat, he began scooping up survivors, then plunged into the bay again and again to rescue others. When some of the now-panicky swimmers grabbed him around the neck, he simply clambered up the side of the barge, carrying them to safety.

Among the first survivors aboard were Cheryl and Joe Saiter, McDonald's neighbors. McDonald was as astonished as they, but there was no time for greetings.

The plane, whose cabin top and tail still jutted above the waves, was now resting on the bay bottom in some 13 feet of water—a final bit of luck that helped spare additional lives. McDonald could see no more swimmers, but heard frantic cries from the opposite side of the wreck. To circle the airliner would take too long. Holding his breath, McDonald pulled the barge back over the 727's sunken left wing and tucked the *Little Mac's* flying bridge snugly beneath the tail's horizontal sta- bilizer. Aware that a scrape could touch off an explosion, he brought the starboard side of the barge parallel to the fuselage and, with superb seamanship, held it there.

Kenney thrust a heavy plank across the gap between the barge and the plane's cabin top about 10 feet away. Racing across the narrow, springy bridge, he threw looped ropes to the survivors struggling in the waves on the other side of the wreck. He and the men on the plane roof began pulling people up, then taking them across the plank to the barge. Several times Kenney—nearing exhaustion, his eyes and lungs hurting from the fuel in the water—dived from the cabin roof to drag in people who couldn't make it to the ropes. One of the last to be plucked from the bay was Mildred Killinger, 68. Mc- Donald again was awed by the strangeness of the night's events. Mrs. Killinger was an old acquaintance, mother of a close childhood friend.

About 50 minutes after the crash, other boats began arriving at the scene. But most of the rescue operation was over. *Little Mac's* two-man crew had picked up 54 of the 58 crash victims.

With a sigh of relief, McDonald and Kenney watched as official craft—swift, maneuverable, far less dangerous to swimmers than their clumsy rig—took over mopping-up op- erations. (About an hour later, a Coast Guard launch rescued a 55th survivor, a woman who had drifted a quarter mile from the crash. Still later, searchers, combing the water around the sunken plane, discovered three bodies.)

Its improbable adventure ended, the *Little Mac* chugged off into the fog to anchor at the damaged railroad bridge. Expecting no credit and wanting none, its skipper and mate had not both- ered to identify themselves to the Marine Patrol. They started the repair job promptly on schedule at 6 a.m. About 6:45, the bridge superintendent shouted, "Hey, what's going on? There's a bunch of newspaper and TV people to see you. They say you and Kenney are heroes."

Thus, national attention was loosed on two shy and aston- ished tugboat men. Their achievement was acknowledged in everything from newspaper headlines to a commendation from President Carter. The seamen were pleased but somewhat embarrassed. "What happened," says Glenn McDonald, "was both a mystery and a miracle—all those twists of chance that dropped those people right beside Kenney and me. I don't think we had anything to do with it. The Lord put us there."

The Unexplained

The Strange Story
of Hector, the Stowaway Dog

by Captain Kenneth Dodson

SECOND OFFICER Harold Kildall of the S. S. *Hanley* noticed
the dog first. The *Hanley,* an Admiral-Oriental Line freighter,
was one of five ships loading at a dock in Vancouver, B.C.,
on April 20, 1922. Inspecting chain lashings, Kildall glanced
up to see a large smooth-haired terrier, white with black mark-
ings, coming aboard by the gangplank. Once aboard, the dog
stood perfectly still, looking and listening all about the deck.
He sniffed at the fresh-sawn timbers of the deckload and at the
sacked grain being loaded into the last hatch. Then he returned
ashore, only to board the next ship, which was loading apples,
flour and fir logs for England. Here the terrier again sniffed
at the cargo and about the decks and living quarters, then slowly
went ashore.

The inspections seemed so deliberate and purposeful that
Kildall's interest was roused. Now he watched the dog board
a freighter loading paper pulp for East Coast ports. The dog
boarded the other ships in turn, examining each in the same
intent fashion. After that, busy with preparations for sea, Kildall forgot the episode. And at noon the *Hanley* got under way
for the long passage to Japan.

Early the next morning the dog was found lying on a coco
mat outside the cabin of the *Hanley*'s captain. Unseen, he had
come aboard again and stowed away for the voyage. The captain, who loved dogs, tried to be friendly, but the terrier would

97

not warm up to his overtures. Kildall and others tried, too, to win him over. To all of them he remained dignified and cool. He merely walked about the captain's deck, sniffing the salt air.

Late that first morning, when Kildall went below to eat, the dog followed him and stood at the galley door, waiting expectantly. The cook gave him his best morsels, which the dog ate as if his due. When Kildall climbed to the bridge to take over the watch, the dog followed close behind, walked through the pilothouse, took a turn through the chartroom, then ran up the ladder to the flying bridge and stood beside the compass binnacle. Apparently satisfied, he lay down in a comfortable corner. Obviously this stowaway was an old sea dog.

For 18 days the *Hanley* plowed across the northern rim of the Pacific. Day after day her officers and men tried to make up to the dog, but he was exasperatingly aloof. He allowed his head to be patted but showed no return of affection. When not "on watch" with Kildall, he remained at the captain's door, going below decks only for his meals.

When the coast of Honshu was sighted, the stowaway sniffed the land breeze and watched intently as the land came abeam. His interest grew as the *Hanley* proceeded through the Yokohama breakwaters to her anchorage near the Customs Jetty. Here the freighter found herself among a number of anchored ships unloading cargos.

While supervising cargo work, Kildall noticed that the dog was remarkably alert, his tail switching from time to time and his nostrils quivering nervously as he peered at the other ships. The nearest of these, the S.S. *Simaloer* of the Nederland Line, was, like the *Hanley*, unloading squared timbers into the harbor.

Soon the *Hanley* swung with the tide so that her stern pointed in the direction of the Dutch ship, now some 300 yards distant. At once the dog's interest centered on her. He ran aft to the fantail, as close to her as possible, and sniffed the air with rising excitement. While Kildall watched, a sampan came alongside the *Simaloer*, took two men aboard, shoved off and sculled for the Customs Landing on a course which carried the craft close under the *Hanley's* stern.

Whining softly, the dog watched. Suddenly he began prancing back and forth in wild excitement, barking madly. This caught the attention of the two passengers in the sampan. Shading their eyes against the sun, they stared at the *Hanley*'s stern.

Presently one of them jumped to his feet and began shouting and waving his arms, motioning to the sampan man and slapping his companion on the back. His excitement matched the dog's. Now, as the sampan came alongside the *Hanley*'s accommodation ladder, the dog became so worked up that he jumped into the water. The shouting man pulled him aboard the sampan and hugged him close, wet coat and all. The dog whined with joy and licked his face. Obviously a dog and his master had been reunited.

The reunion of the stowaway and his happy owner became the talk of the crews of both ships. The dog's name, it turned out, was Hector. His owner, W.H. Mante, second officer of the *Simaloer*, had the same duties and the same watches to stand as Kildall had on the *Hanley*. Leaving the dock in Vancouver, the *Simaloer* had shifted berth for bunkering while Hector was off for a last run before the long voyage. Mante's frantic search of the waterfront failed to locate Hector in time— and the *Simaloer* sailed without him.

What mysterious instinct could have governed Hector's methodical search for the one ship out of many which would carry him across an ocean to rejoin his beloved master? Did the character of the *Hanley*'s cargo and perhaps other signs tell him that the *Hanley* was bound for the same destination as his own ship? Did he then attach himself to the officer whose duties were like his master's? Any answers would be the guesswork of men, who know only what happened.

Houdini, the Man
No Lock Could Hold

by James Stewart-Gordon

IN MAY 1903, Harry Houdini was appearing at a Moscow cabaret. To publicize his act, he called on Lebedev, the gigantic bearded chief of Moscow's secret police. Houdini asked to be put in jail to demonstrate how easily he could escape. Lebedev, who knew of Houdini's reputation, smilingly refused. "How about the Carette then?" Houdini suggested.

Lebedev laughed. The Carette—a six-foot-square, steel-sheathed cube—was used to transport dangerous criminals to Siberia. It had only two openings—a tiny barred window, just eight inches square, and a solid-steel door. The key which locked the Carette's door in Moscow activated a device which could be opened only by a second key, kept by the prison governor in Siberia 2000 miles away. "No one has ever escaped from the Carette," Lebedev told Houdini. "I accept your challenge. But once we lock you up, you will have to be sent to Siberia to be released."

"I'll get out," Houdini insisted.

Stripped naked, searched for concealed picklocks, handcuffed and chained, Houdini was shoved into the tiny cell. The cell was then locked and moved so that its door was hidden against a wall in the prison yard. Twenty-eight minutes later, dripping with sweat, Houdini staggered out from behind the cell. Amazed, the police rushed to examine the Carette. The seal on its door was intact, the handcuffs and chains which had bound the prisoner were still locked. But Houdini was free.

Harry Houdini—escape artist, magician, author of more than 40 books, inventor, film star, aviator, showman and psychologist—swept through the world like a hurricane between 1895 and 1926, leaving behind him a trail of vanquished prison cells, vacated handcuffs and gasping audiences. Sir Arthur Conan Doyle, creator of Sherlock Holmes, admired him for having "supernatural powers." A reporter in Germany, stunned by the ease with which Houdini was able to free himself from a sealed packing case without disturbing a single nail, declared, "Houdini has the ability to de-materialize his body and pass it through walls." In Washington, D.C., a handcuffed Houdini jauntily escaped from a maximum-security cell in the federal penitentiary. He then playfully moved 18 other locked-up prisoners to different cells before escaping to the outside—all in about 27 minutes.

Behind every exercise of Houdini's art was a painstaking attention to detail. To prepare for his demolition of claims that Indian fakirs possessed supernatural powers enabling them to be buried alive, he spent endless hours nailed inside a box while assistants timed his ability to remain conscious with a limited supply of oxygen. Finally satisfied that he could match the fakirs' performance, he climbed into a coffin, crossed hands on his breast and allowed himself to be sealed inside. An hour and a half later he was released, pale but very much alive. Snorting at suggestions of supernatural powers, he told reporters, "It's just a trick. I don't eat or drink for 24 hours beforehand and I remain absolutely still; that way I don't use up much oxygen."

In his pursuit and exposure of fake spirit mediums, Houdini was relentless. His most famous case revolved around the blond, beautiful Boston medium, Margery. So convincing was her performance—which featured a bell box under the séance table by which the spirits supposedly answered questions—that the staid and lofty *Scientific American* was prepared to pay her its prize of $2500 for genuine contact with the world of spooks. In July 1924, Houdini—who himself made an open offer of $10,000 to any medium who produced psychic phenomena he could not duplicate by natural means—canceled a stage engagement and journeyed to Boston to challenge Margery. Stipulating that he was to be seated next to the medium, Houdini sensitized his right leg—which was to be pressed against Margery's left during the séance—by binding it below the knee with a tight elastic bandage on the morning of the séance. By séance time, the leg was so tender it could detect a butterfly's sneeze at ten paces. After the lights went out and Margery had gone into her trance, Houdini edged up his trouser leg, exposing his bare skin to Margery's silken calf. When Margery made an all-but-imperceptible move of her foot to press a hidden button—a maneuver Houdini had long suspected—the master's leg vibrated like a well-struck gong. Jumping to his feet, Houdini proclaimed Margery a fake, denounced the entire affair and went back to his stage work with his $10,000, and *Scientific American*'s $2500, still intact.

Offstage, Houdini was a shy, diminutive man (just five feet five inches), who wore rumpled suits and spoke in a mess of mangled verbs and tenses. Onstage, however, everything changed. Houdini seemed to swell to giant's stature; his gray-blue eyes glowed, his diction became impeccable, his clothing was immaculate and his mastery of his craft so outstanding that, as the late Fulton Oursler said, "That man could escape from anything—except your memory."

The Great Houdini was born Ehrich Weiss in Budapest, Hungary, in 1874, the fifth of eight children of a poor rabbi who immigrated to Wisconsin when Ehrich was still an infant. As a small boy, Ehrich sold newspapers, shined shoes and worked in a Milwaukee luggage shop where, during his free time, he liked to tinker with the locks on trunks and valises. At 16, after reading the autobiography of Robert-Houdin, the great 19th-century French magician and diplomat, he began to dream of becoming a great magician himself. When he was 17, the family resettled in New York, and Harry Houdini, as he now called himself, became an apprentice cutter in a tie factory during the day and a magician whenever someone would hire him for an evening or weekend show. Using a friend or his brother Theo as his partner in a spectacular quick-switch trunk escape, Harry played firemen's picnics, boilermakers' soirees and lodge halls.

In June 1894, he met a young Brooklyn girl named Bess Rahner, and married her after a two-day courtship. The marriage lasted 32 happy years, until Houdini's death.

In 1900, convinced that he was ready for the big time, Houdini took his act to New York. But New York was indifferent. Stung, Houdini told Bess, "Pack your bags. We're going to London." There Harry approached the manager of the Alhambra Theatre—the city's most important music hall—showed him his scrapbook and asked for a tryout. The manager was unimpressed by Houdini's success with American handcuffs. "Go down to Scotland Yard," he said, "and if you can get out of *their* handcuffs I might give you a try."

Houdini went to "The Yard," and persuaded a detective superintendent to put him to the test. The detective led Harry to a pillar, handcuffed him to it, put on his hat and announced that he was going to lunch. "Wait a second!" Harry yelled after him, "I'll go with you!" Handing the opened handcuffs to the astonished inspector, he took his arm and led him through the door.

The story made every paper in England, and soon Harry's fame as "the man no fetter, no lock, no restraint can hold" spread all over Europe. In 1905, he came back to New York a celebrity.

The year 1913 marked a turning point for Houdini. His mother, who had been a profound force in his life, died while he was en route to Copenhagen. Unable to reconcile himself either to her loss or to his failure to be at her deathbed, he swallowed his skepticism and began to visit mediums and spiritualists in the hope of communicating with her. Each medium he visited proved a charlatan. The final straw came when, during one séance, a voice—speaking in Oxford-accented English—assured Harry that she was his mother and that she was happy in the "other world." Houdini's mother had never learned much English, and what little she did speak was unmistakably tinged with a Yiddish accent. Furious, Houdini launched into a savage crusade which made him the terror of every table-rapper and séance fraud.

In 1923, at the age of 50, Houdini began to talk of retirement. His popularity, bolstered by film appearances, had never been higher. Yet he was filled with an impending sense of death. He saw omens in strange happenings: the unexplained sound of his mother calling his name, the bizarre reactions of animals in his presence. In New York, on a rainy night in October 1926, he phoned Joseph Dunninger, the famous magician and mentalist, and asked him to come to his house. When Dunninger arrived, Houdini explained that he wanted Dunninger to help him take some boxes to a storage place on the other side of the city. As they were driving away, Houdini suddenly told Dunninger to turn back. They arrived before the house, and Houdini got out of the car. He stood silently in the rain and then got back in. "I just wanted one last look," Houdini said. "I'll never see it again alive."

Houdini left soon after on a U.S. and Canadian tour. In Montreal, he gave a lecture at McGill University on the fakery of spiritualism. His talk infuriated local mediums, who were unanimous in denouncing him. On the morning of his final appearance in Montreal, he was lying exhausted on the couch in his dressing room when several students who had been at his lecture arrived. One of them, who wanted to sketch Houdini, had been invited. The others had come without invitation. Suddenly, one of the uninvited guests began to question Houdini's views on spiritualism. Too tired to argue, Houdini tried to placate the visitor, but only succeeded in arousing him. "Is it true," the man cried, "that you are so strong you can take a punch anywhere on your body without injury?" Houdini mumbled vaguely, and before he could prepare himself the man began raining sledgehammer blows on his solar plexus.

Although badly hurt, Houdini refused to show it; in fact, he went onstage for that day's performance. But the next few days were a confusion of agony as he seemed to weave in and out of consciousness. In Detroit, he collapsed and was taken to Grace Hospital, suffering from a ruptured appendix and peritonitis. Bess, who had also been sick, now joined her husband in the hospital. On October 29, a fading Houdini struggled with his final problem. "Mother never reached me," he gasped to Bess. "If anything happens you must be prepared. Remember this message: 'Rosabelle, believe.'" Shortly afterward, Houdini was dead—strangely enough, on Halloween.

But his death did not end the story. Throughout the years that followed, the same mediums whose tricks Houdini had so industriously exposed began reporting that they were the recipients of messages sent by Houdini from the Great Beyond. "If Houdini keeps this message stuff up," commented Will Rogers, "he's going to put Western Union out of business."

For the next ten years, Bess, on the anniversary of his death, sat in their home before a candle-lit portrait of the master, and waited for his signal. It never came. In 1936, ten years after his death, she extinguished the light.

But among magicians there are still those who go out each year at Halloween to the place where Houdini is buried to pay their respects.

Oak Island's Legendary "Money Pit"

by David MacDonald

JUST OFF the rugged southern shore of Nova Scotia lies a tiny island shaped somewhat like a question mark. The shape is appropriate, for little Oak Island is the scene of a baffling whodunit that has defied solution for almost two centuries. Here, ever since 1795—not long after pirates prowled the Atlantic Coast and left glittering legends of buried gold in their wake—people have been trying to find out what lies at the bottom of a mysterious shaft dubbed, hopefully, the "Money Pit."

Using picks and shovels, divining rods and drilling rigs, treasure hunters have poured more than $1,500,000 *into* the Money Pit. To date, they have taken precious little out—only three links of gold chain and a scrap of ancient parchment. Despite more than 20 attempts, no one has yet reached bottom: each time a digging or drilling crew has seemed close to success, torrents of water have suddenly surged into the shaft to drown their hopes. Although it's now known that the Money Pit is protected by an ingenious system of man-made flood tunnels that use the sea as a watchdog, to this day no one knows who dug the pit, or why.

One legend makes the pit the hiding place for the plunder of Captain Kidd, who was hanged for piracy in 1701. Other theories favor the booty of Blackbeard and Henry Morgan, both notorious buccaneers; or Inca treasure stolen by Spaniards;

or the French crown jewels that Louis XVI and Marie Antoinette were said to be carrying when they attempted to flee during the French Revolution; or Shakespeare's missing manuscripts. Whatever the pit may contain, few other treasures have been sought so avidly.

The long parade of searchers began one day more than 185 years ago, when Daniel McInnes, a 16-year-old boy from Chester, Nova Scotia, paddled over to uninhabited Oak Island to hunt for game. On a knoll at one end of the island he noticed an odd depression, 12 feet in diameter. Sixteen feet above it, on a sawed-off tree limb, hung an old ship's tackleblock. McInnes's heart raced, for in the nearby port of La Have, once a lair for pirates preying on New England shipping, he had heard many legends of buried treasure.

Next day he came back with two other boys, Tony Vaughan and Jack Smith, and began digging. Ten feet down they hit a platform of aged oak logs; at 20 feet, another; at 30, a third. In the flinty clay walls of the shaft they could still see the marks of pickaxes. As the work grew harder, they sought help. But no one else would go near Oak Island. It was said to be haunted by the ghosts of two fishermen who vanished there in 1720 while investigating strange lights. So the boys gave up, temporarily.

Later, McInnes and Smith settled on the island. In 1804, intrigued by their tale, a wealthy Nova Scotian named Simeon Lynds joined them in forming a treasure company. They again found oak tiers every ten feet down the pit, to a depth of 90 feet. They also uncovered layers of tropical coconut fiber, charcoal and ship's putty, plus a stone cut with curious symbols that one cryptologist took to mean, *"Ten feet below, two million pounds are buried."* At 93 feet, the diggers drove a crowbar five feet deeper and struck a solid mass. Lynds felt sure that it was a treasure chest.

But next morning he was amazed to find 60 feet of water in the pit. Weeks of bailing proved fruitless; the water level remained constant. Lynds assumed that this was due to an underground freshwater spring. The next year, his hired miners dug 110 feet down, off to one side of the Money Pit, then began burrowing toward it. When they were only two feet from it, tons of water burst through. As they scrambled for their lives, the shaft quickly filled to the same depth as the Money Pit.

Beaten and almost broke, Lynds gave up. McInnes died. But Vaughan and Smith never lost hope. In 1849, they took another stab at the Money Pit, with a syndicate from Truro, Nova Scotia. The results were dramatic.

At 98 feet down, just where the crowbar had hit a solid mass in 1804, a horse-driven pod auger (which picked up a sample of anything it passed through) pierced a spruce platform. After dropping through an empty space, it cut into four inches of oak, 22 inches of metal pieces, eight of oak, 22 of loose metal again, four more inches of oak and six of spruce, and then into deep clay. To the drillers this suggested an exciting prospect—a vault containing two chests, one atop the other and laden with treasure, perhaps gold coins or jewels. Moreover, the auger brought up a tantalizing sample of what might be there: three links of a gold chain!

A second 110-foot shaft was dug in 1850. It also flooded. But this time a workman fell in and came up sputtering, "Salt water!" Then someone noticed that the water in the pits rose and fell like the tide. This discovery jogged old Tony Vaughan's memory: years before, he had seen water gushing down the beach at Smith's Cove—520 feet from the Money Pit—at low tide.

The treasure hunters stripped the sandy beach, searching for a hidden inlet of the sea. Under the sand, to their astonishment, they found tons of coconut fiber and eel grass on a stone floor that stretched, 154 feet wide, the full distance between high- and low-tide marks. More digging uncovered more surprises: five rock-walled box drains slanted in from the sea and down, converging on a line aimed at the Money Pit.

In effect, the beach acted as a gigantic sponge to soak up tidewater and filter it into a conduit. This conduit dropped 70 feet straight down, later exploration proved, then sloped back to a point deep in the Money Pit—all of it filled with loose rock to prevent erosion. This brilliant baffle was no natural obstacle; it was the work of a genius. As diggers neared the cache at 98 feet, they had unwittingly lessened the pressure of earth that plugged the mouth of the conduit.

Undeterred, the Truro crew built a cofferdam to hold back the sea. The sea promptly wrecked it. Next they dug 118 feet down and burrowed *under* the Money Pit. But while the diggers were at dinner, the bottom of the pit collapsed into the tunnel, then dropped even farther—into a mysteriously empty space.

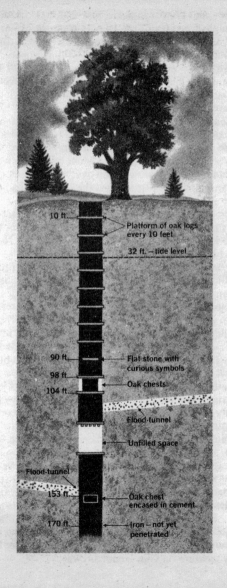

10 ft. — Platform of oak logs every 10 feet

32 ft. — tide level

90 ft. — Flat stone with curious symbols

98 ft. — Oak chests

104 ft.

Flood-tunnel

Unfilled space

Flood-tunnel

153 ft. — Oak chest encased in cement

170 ft. — Iron — not yet penetrated

Though the Truro syndicate lost $40,000, its discoveries excited wide interest in Oak Island. A series of costly expeditions followed, all dogged by bad luck. One outfit gave up after a huge steam pump exploded, killing a man. In 1893, almost a century after the dig began, still another syndicate was organized, this time by Frederick Blair, a Nova Scotia businessman who was to spend almost 60 years trying to solve the mystery.

His company was the first to locate the flood-tunnel outlet, 111 feet down the side of the Money Pit. To block it at the source, dynamite was set off deep underground near the shore at Smith's Cove. After filling the Money Pit with water, well above sea level, Blair threw in red dye. Not a trace of it seeped back to Smith's Cove—proof that the dynamite had been successful.

But on the *opposite* shore of the island, 300 feet from the pit, red stains appeared at three places! This meant that there was at least one more flood tunnel to cope with. No one has yet found it.

Blair and his partners also resorted to core-drilling in the Money Pit. At 153 feet—the deepest yet—their bit chewed into seven inches of cement, five of oak, 32 inches of metal pieces, then more oak and cement. Finally, at 170 feet, it rattled against impenetrable iron.

To Blair, this indicated a treasure chest encased in primitive concrete, larger and buried deeper than the ones drilled through in 1850. This time, along with flecks of gold, the bit brought up a tiny scrap of parchment bearing the letters *vi*—written with a quill pen and India ink, according to analysts in Boston. "That's more convincing than a few doubloons would be, " Blair claimed. "Either a treasure of immense value or priceless historical documents are at the bottom of that pit." But the syndicate never found out. After spending more than $100,000, it folded.

Only Blair carried on. He secured treasure-trove rights to the island for 40 years, then offered to lease them for a share in any bonanza that might be found. The first taker was engineer Harry Bowdoin, of New York. With several prominent backers looking on—including a young lawyer named Franklin D. Roosevelt—Bowdoin dug and drilled in 1909, to no avail. Then he wrote a magazine article, claiming that there had never been any treasure on Oak Island anyway.

Next came syndicates from Wisconsin, Rochester, N.Y., and Newark, N.J. All failed. In 1931, William Chappell, of Sydney, Nova Scotia, a wealthy contractor who had run the drill that bought up the piece of parchment, sank $30,000 into the Money Pit. Then the Depression made him quit.

Chappell was followed in 1936 by Gilbert Hedden, a New Jersey millionaire who spent $100,000 more. Hedden ran submarine power lines from the mainland to drive high-speed pumps, and hired a Pennsylvania mining firm to clear the 170-foot shaft. He finally concluded that all the digging and flooding had probably shifted the treasure as much as 100 feet—in *any* direction.

At the time of Blair's death in 1951, Oak Island and its treasure rights were acquired by William Chappell's son, Mel, who had worked with his father's expedition in 1931. Mel Chappell spent $25,000 on one excavation, which quickly became a small lake, then leased portions of his rights to a series of other fortune hunters, including the late Bob Restall, of Hamilton, Ontario. Then a 59-year-old steelworker, Restall quit his $150-a-week job in 1959 and moved to Oak Island with his wife, Mildred, and their sons, Bobby and Rickey, then 23 and 15.

Until his death the family lived in a one-room cabin beside the Money Pit, a caved-in crater filled with sludge and rotting timbers. Restall managed to clear a 155-foot shaft sunk in the 1930s. He added eight holes, 25 feet deep, trying to intercept the flood tunnels that have foiled all previous searches.

To finance his hunt, Restall sold about half of his half-interest in any treasure to friends and interested strangers who had written from as far away as Texas. In all, including his savings and five years of hard labor, Restall figured that his quest for Oak Island's elusive hoard cost almost $100,000. Yet all he found was an olive-colored stone chiseled with the date "1704," which he found in one of the holes, and a profound respect for whoever designed the Money Pit. "That man," he said, "was one hell of a lot smarter than anyone who has come here since."

Is there really a treasure at the bottom of the Money Pit? According to mining experts, its elaborate safeguards could have been built only by an engineering wizard with plenty of help—and plenty to hide. As petroleum engineer George Greene put it in 1955, after drilling on Oak Island for a syndicate of Texas oilmen, *"Someone* went to a lot of trouble to bury *something* here. And unless he was the greatest practical joker of all time, it must have been well worth the effort."

Is There Life After Death?

by Mary Ann O'Roark

VIRGINIA FALCE was undergoing a routine tonsillectomy when her heart stopped. "All of a sudden I was rising through a white mist," she recalls. "Then it was all dark. I wasn't frightened— a little curious, I guess. I felt a sense of absolute love and peace embracing me, coming from a glowing circle of light. I wasn't a churchgoer—I didn't believe in it. But I knew this light was God, and it was such love and joy that I wanted to go to it forever. Then the thought came that I had two children. I had a job to do and I *had* to return."

Hospital records show that doctors performed immediate surgery on Mrs. Falce, cutting open her chest to massage her heart by hand. "The next thing I remember," she says, "was the nurse standing over me and later on doctors and nurses coming in and asking me what it was like to die."

Accounts such as this are not new: they have been quietly heard for years. What is new is a readiness on the part of physicians and scholars to listen to them seriously and to study them as legitimate data worthy of professional research. Today, scientists who once might have regarded these accounts with skepticism are becoming increasingly convinced of their authenticity.

Dr. Elisabeth Kübler-Ross, a psychiatrist and author of *On Death and Dying*, has lectured on the many cases in which people close to death reported "heavenly" experiences. And in

1975, Dr. Raymond A. Moody, Jr., published *Life After Life*,
in which he reported over a hundred such cases he had encountered in his career.

As compelling as their stories were, they had not been re-
searched and recorded according to rigorous scientific and
medical procedures. The question was, would such stories stand
up under close scrutiny? Both baffled and fascinated by these
accounts, University of Connecticut psychologist and professor
Kenneth Ring set out to find an entirely new group of people
who had come close to death, and to collect and scientifically
verify information about them.

In the course of his research, he found that his subjects—
men and women of a wide range of age, education, background
and temperament—all spoke of what he called a "core experience," which occurred when they were close to death or
clinically dead. They told of being outside of, or separated
from their bodies, of communicating with deceased loved ones,
of gliding down a dark tunnel toward a lustrous light, of reaching a threshold but drawing back from it, sometimes because
of a feeling of responsibility toward others. Although there
were variations in the accounts, the responses were always
similar: there was a sense of great comfort and even bliss in
which the person longed to remain and whose positive intensity
was carried back to affect the rest of that person's life in the
"earthly" world.

Regardless of what their attitudes had been before—and
their religious beliefs varied widely—most of these people
were convinced they had been in the presence of some supreme
and loving power and had been given a glimpse of a life yet
to come.

Throughout his research, Ring checked certain factors.
Could these stories have been induced by drugs or anesthesia?
Possibly, but in many instances the subjects had had no drugs
at all; in other cases, the anesthesia and medications used
seemed unlikely to have caused reactions like the ones described. If anything, Ring believes, drugs and anesthetics may
cause a person to forget a near-death experience.

Were these experiences hallucinations brought about by
toxic shock? Again, this could be a factor, but hallucinations
are rambling, unconnected, and differ widely, depending on
the individual; these stories were clear, consistent, and grounded
in a sense of reality. As a psychiatrist who had one of these

experiences told Ring, she was well aware of what constituted a dream or a hallucination—and this was neither.

Do people facing the end of their lives see what they *want* to see? Not necessarily. Some of Ring's subjects had no advance warning that their lives were in danger, and many of them had done no wishful thinking about a pleasant afterlife. (This was true in particular of 36 attempted suicides Ring studied—most of whom had hoped to end their consciousness altogether.)

Finally, was this "glimpse of death" just a brief, bizarre episode—something like a flash of extrasensory perception before the phone rings? Apparently not. These experiences seem to have caused a transformation in the lives of those who went through them, in their attitudes and values, their inclination to love and to help others. "I'm convinced," says Ring, "that these are absolutely authentic experiences."

Perhaps the greatest number of medically detailed cases has been collected over the past 19 years by Dr. Fred W. Schoonmaker, Director of Cardiovascular Services at St. Luke's Hospital in Denver. He has amassed medical records and case histories of 2300 patients who came close to death. Of that number, more than 1400 reported having near-death experiences similar to those in Ring's study.

Some of this testimony is shrugged off by skeptics who cite the cause to be cerebral anoxia—lack of oxygen to the brain. However, sophisticated equipment was used at St. Luke's to monitor patients' vital signs. Records show that enough oxygen continued to be present for adequate brain function. Abnormal electrical impulses racing in the brain during its final minutes are also often given as a possible reason for near-death experiences. Yet in a number of Schoonmaker's cases the electroencephalograph readings (EEGs that report on the brain's activity) were "flat," or nonexistent, for periods ranging from 30 minutes to three hours, well beyond the time at which a person is considered clinically dead—but from which patients returned to consciousness, sometimes inexplicably, to report experiences of peace, comfort and beauty.

"Most physicians don't hear these stories," says Dr. Michael Sabom, assistant professor of cardiology at Emory University in Atlanta. "People are afraid doctors and others will laugh at them, so they keep the experiences to themselves." Sabom himself would have been one of the first to dismiss them. "I read Raymond Moody's book when it first came out," he says, "and I was very skeptical. But I was in cardiovascular training at the University of Florida Medical School at the time, and routinely dealt with people who were in cardiac arrest, so a psychiatric social worker and I started to check out these phenomena for ourselves."

Over the past four years Sabom has investigated 120 cases in which patients had close brushes with death. What specifically interested him were out-of-body experiences, in which people reported leaving their unconscious bodies to observe from another vantage point, usually from above, what was happening. "When I started to check out these stories," Sabom says, "I found that some of the patients could tell me in detail, in the correct sequence, exactly what had happened to their bodies on the operating table. One man described how he floated above his body and watched the operating team at work. He described the instruments, how the heart looked, and the operative procedure itself. I was amazed—there was nothing in his background to indicate that he could have picked up this medical knowledge otherwise. In another case, a man's heart had stopped beating for four to five minutes, and he described—exactly—what went on during that time. To me, this is the strongest evidence that these weren't just hallucinations or fantasies. There's something going on here, and it can't be explained in traditional ways."

But disbelievers continue to try. They theorize that a sense of isolation and anxiety sends the mind into protective shock; that the ego, faced with destruction, reacts to the unbearable stress with a last mighty act of denial. Some insist that the powerful trauma of death triggers the powerful memory of birth, and that the movement down a tunnel of darkness to an awaiting light is only a flashback to another time of transition.

However, serious near-death researchers say such "explanations" are superficial and simplistic. Sociologist John Audette, executive director of the International Association for Near-Death Studies, says, "It's true that some of the cases can possibly be explained by biochemical or physiological conditions. But such facts don't begin to account for the large number and wide range of these experiences—and if skeptical researchers would study our cases in depth, they, too, would see that."

Medical investigators now see these cases as lessons for the living. It is why they hope the public will evaluate them thoughtfully, and not rush to romanticize death or to seek it out. Says Kenneth Ring: "One result of these experiences is that people 'come back' convinced that human life is precious, that it's wrong to violate the natural order of things by ending one's own life deliberately." Dr. Bruce Greyson, assistant professor of psychiatry at the University of Michigan Medical Center in Ann Arbor, has studied more than 150 near-death stories in the Michigan area. His current focus is on attempted suicides. He has found that "people who live through these experiences come out of them with a real sense of purpose in their lives. Although death is no longer fearful, life has become more meaningful."

While it is the personal conviction of many researchers that human consciousness does survive and continue on into another realm, they make it clear that each person must decide for himself. "It's up to each individual to integrate this information into his or her own life," says Dr. Moody. Adds Michael Sabom: "Whether these experiences continue after a certain point is pure speculation. For those who have been close to actual physical death, there's no doubt about it—they're convinced that they have had a look at what is to come."

Dr. Ian Stevenson, Carlson Professor of Psychiatry at the University of Virginia Medical Center, who over the past 20 years has studied a variety of evidence suggesting life after death, including many near-death cases, also emphasizes that people must grapple with the data and "judge for themselves." But, personally, Dr. Stevenson speaks for many who have studied this phenomenon when he says, "There is increasing evidence that we do live after death. I think it prudent to prepare for the eventuality."

Ghost Train
on the Main Line!

by E.D. Fales, Jr.

AT 10:29 P.M., on November 12, 1959, a warning bell sounded in HY tower overlooking the sprawling terminal yard of the Jersey Central Railroad, which is now part of Amtrak, in Jersey City. Towerman Joe Hilinski looked up, startled. The bell shouldn't have sounded. No trains were supposed to be moving in the yard. Hilinski spun around to his model board—the 12-foot track diagram on the wall. For a moment he was reassured. Not a track on the board was lighted.

Then a tiny white bulb lighted up on Track 9. Something was coming!

Hilinski peered out into the darkened, silent yard. There were no lights; nothing was moving. He felt his flesh start to creep.

Suddenly Hilinski spotted a dark mass, moving fast. As it neared, he made out the shape of a diesel-electric locomotive, with all lights extinguished. He judged from the roaring sound that it was being driven at full throttle.

"She's going to hit the derail," he gasped. This is a heavy iron wedge clamped to one rail to derail any runaway freight car before it can roll out onto the main line.

The locomotive came to the derail—and the impossible happened. It went right over it. Each wheel sprang eight inches into the air and landed back on the rail. Then the engine blasted out on Main Line Track 3.

Hilinski, stunned, shouted an urgent and seldom-used command into his phone: "Hold on three!" That was an order to stop all trains on Main Line Track 3—a drastic step on a busy 60-mile-an-hour thoroughfare.

Two miles away, Joe's warning cry was heard by his brother, assistant chief dispatcher Frank Hilinski, the night boss.

"What's wrong?" demanded Frank.

Joe's voice shook, "You have a runaway engine, traveling fast, all dark."

"Which way is he headed?"

"West—against traffic."

Frank Hilinski jumped up. Six freights and passengers were rolling on the four main-line tracks within 30 miles of the terminal. The nearest, the eastbound New York *Clocker*, a crack passenger express, was on Track 1, coming fast and due to stop at Bayonne in four minutes. The runaway on Track 3, adjacent to Track 1, would slam through Bayonne just as passengers would be swarming over Track 3 to get to and from the stopped *Clocker*. If the engine plowed into the crowd...

Hilinski quickly ordered Bayonne tower to try to stop the *Clocker* before she entered the station. He also phoned Bayonne yards.

"There's a runaway engine coming your way," he told the startled yardmaster. "Set flares. We don't know what's wrong with the crew."

Perhaps the engineer had fainted, with his foot still heavy on the deadman's pedal. Maybe some drunk had stolen the engine, or a madman was holding the crew at gun point.

The phone rang. The Bayonne yardmaster reported back. "Your engine is No. 1706. Went by here at 10:34. Never slowed down. Couldn't see any crew." No. 1706 was a huge, 123-ton diesel-electric workhorse assigned to yard duty.

At 10:35 the runaway, having covered four miles from HY tower in five minutes, charged without warning through Bayonne station. Passengers waiting for the *Clocker*, now stopped safely outside the station, heard the apparition coming and shrank back in fright. No one was hurt. West of the station, the crew of the halted *Clocker* was astonished to see an engine, all dark, roar past on the wrong side and vanish into the night.

In the next 90 seconds, Frank Hilinski did some fast thinking. The train chart now showed that the runaway was speeding toward a head-on collision, in about 18 minutes, with No. 692, a freight rolling east from Bound Brook. He *had* to get the engine off Track 3 somewhere.

Hilinski turned to a two-track line called the Perth Amboy Branch. It swings away from the main line at a busy junction known as E'port (short for Elizabethport). But both branch tracks were blocked. A Pennsylvania seashore express was barreling north on Track 1. A freight was plodding south on Track 2. However, it would be 30 minutes before the runaway could overtake the freight. Hilinski, playing for time, ordered E'port tower to send the runaway hurtling down the branch on southbound Track 2.

Hilinski now phoned division superintendent Joseph Galuppo at home. The call awakened Galuppo. A normally calm man, he became in the next half-hour, he later testified, almost a nervous wreck.

Hilinski stated the situation briefly. Should he open the Raritan River Draw and dump the engine into the river?

"No!" roared Galuppo. Barges filled with propane used the Raritan. An engine smashing onto a propane barge could set off a devastating explosion.

A voice on the speaker interrupted. It was E'port tower reporting: "Runaway by here. Passing her from Main Line Track 3 to Branch Track 2."

Suddenly superintendent Galuppo, still on the phone with Hilinski, had a daring idea. "Get hold of Jeffrey [trainmaster Ed Jeffrey, at Long Branch, N.J.]," he said.

At this moment the big freight on Branch Track 2 was approaching the Raritan drawbridge, 15 miles south. In command of her engine was Chet Gudmunson, a small white-haired man. Also riding the engine were fireman Harold Johns and head brakeman Leo Barry. At the bridge Gudmunson saw a waving lantern and braked to a stop. The bridge captain shouted, "Your engineer is wanted on the phone in a hurry—Jeffrey's calling."

Gudmunson climbed down and ran to the bridge phone. Trainmaster Jeffrey's voice said, "Don't interrupt! Just listen. Seconds count."

Jeffrey said that a runaway was coming. "We'd like you to cut off your train and proceed immediately to the straight track at South Amboy. We'll switch the runaway from Track 2 to Track 1 to go around our stopped train, then back to Track 2 so he's behind you. When you see him coming up behind, match his speed, then slow down, let him bump you and force him to stop. We'll stop the northbound express at South Amboy."

Gudmunson knew he was being asked, not ordered. This was beyond the call of duty. With retirement coming and a wife at home, he didn't have to risk his life. Neither did Johns or Barry.

Gudmunson consulted with them a few seconds. They'd all go.

By this time, Hilinski had all towers on a single phone circuit. Up and down the line, everyone heard these reports in quick succession:

10:53, from South Amboy tower: "Gudmunson passing southbound, moving slowly, ten miles an hour."

10:54, from Barber tower: "Runaway by here fast on Track 2. Speed is 45."

10:55, from Woodbridge tower: "I just switched runaway over to Track 1. She nearly dumped, but she made it."

Then, at 10:58, from South Amboy tower, disturbing news: "Gudmunson has stopped!"

At this moment, the runaway was only a mile behind.

Gudmunson was worried. He had proceeded one-half mile to the straight track at South Amboy, as ordered. Then, feeling a desperate need for more information, he had stopped at a trackside telephone. Brakeman Barry went to the track phone for instructions. There had been no time for the voice at the bridge to tell Gudmunson one important fact: The runaway was running dark. So the three crewmen, staring back into the empty blackness of a tunnel through which they had just passed, were all watching for something they would never see: a headlight.

At the Raritan drawbridge, the crew of Gudmunson's train, mystified at being left behind by their engine, heard a roar behind them. At 10:57 the runaway skinned past them on Track 1 and across Raritan Draw.

Ahead of the runaway, a switch slid and locked. The runaway's speed tape later showed that she hit this 10-m.p.h. switch at 46 m.p.h. She lurched, leaned over hard, made a slamming turn and settled down on southbound Track 2. The passenger train was now safe. But the runaway was only a half-mile behind Gudmunson and his parked engine.

Ahead, to the south, Gudmunson could see the express lying in South Amboy station with its headlight blazing. Normally, it would have been dimmed. Gudmunson didn't know that the engineer had been ordered: "Keep your light on so it will shine on the runaway."

Peering at the darkened tunnel, Gudmunson suddenly saw the faintest glimmer of light—the dim reflection of the express train's headlight on the runaway. The engine was right on them.

Johns shouted for Barry as Gudmunson reached for the throttle.

A diesel builds up power slowly—you can't rush it. Gudmunson eased the lever back an inch; then he gave her quarter throttle and she began to roll. Within ten seconds, he risked half throttle, and the engine shook. When his speedometer said 35, he gave full throttle.

They flew past the express waiting in South Amboy station. Just ahead lay a sharp S-curve. "I've got to do it now," Gudmunson decided. With his speed at 60, he began shutting down and valving air. The runaway was dangerously close.

Head brakeman Barry thought Gudmunson slowed too much. Barry shouted, "Hold on hard—it's going to ram us!" Gudmunson yanked the throttle open—but too late. The collision was deafening. Steel motor-hood doors all along the catwalk burst open. Barry and Johns were slammed into their seats.

The couplers had met and locked. Gudmunson shut off power, but was afraid to apply hard brakes; his engine might cartwheel in front of the heavier runaway.

Johns, holding the handrail, crept back along the rocking catway. The heavy steel doors—ten of them—kept slamming in his way. Flashlight in hand, he closed each door, swung to the other engine and into the cab. There was no one there. He flashed his light on the controls. Everything was perfectly set for running: throttle pulled back full, air brakes set for running. The isolation switch—which can cut generator power from the wheel motors—was on. He shut the throttle and heard No. 1706 die. Then he set the brakes and flipped on the cab light. Instantly he felt Gudmunson apply full braking power to wrestle the runaway to a halt.

The two engines slid to a stop in a cloud of hot sand and smoke. Gudmunson proceeded to the nearest phone. He lifted the receiver and all along the line, from Jeffrey at Long Branch up to Hilinski at Jersey City, they heard his voice: "This is Gudmunson. We got her."

"How's her crew?" someone asked.

"Crew?" said Gudmunson. "She's got no crew. She's a bloody ghost."

THE MYSTERY is still unsolved. The FBI and New Jersey's Public Utilities Commission immediately investigated. The runaway had been parked, awaiting a new crew, with its engine idling, standard practice in cold weather. The locomotive had taken off within two minutes of the time her crew left her. What happened in those two minutes?

Several theories were considered—and exploded. Had someone tried to steal or wreck the engine? There were no clues, no fingerprints. Besides, it would have taken an expert to know the complicated starting procedure.

Had the throttle vibrated open by itself? This has been known to happen on some engines, but P.U.C. tests showed it couldn't have on No. 1706. Even if it had, who shifted the engine from neutral into gear, released the air brakes, put the isolation switch on "run"?

Had the runaway been carelessly parked? Her crew, all veterans with good records, testified they had carefully gone through the eight-step shutdown routine.

One safety precaution resulted. Locks were installed in all Jersey Central engines, like the ignition lock of a car. Locked in neutral, the engine could be idled—but not moved.

No. 1706 had covered 22 miles in a frightening adventure that lasted exactly 36 minutes. She had given one of America's railroads a fright it will never forget.

The Enduring Mystery
of Jack the Ripper

by James Stewart-Gordon

IN THE early-morning hours of August 31, 1888, a killer slipped out of the London Fog, slashed a woman to death, mutilated her corpse, then vanished. During the next ten weeks he struck four more times, each time growing more bold and bloody. Then he disappeared, and has not been heard from since.

Who this killer—"Jack the Ripper"—was, why he killed and how he escaped have never been determined, and his incredible tale has grown into the most enduring criminal puzzle of all time. So horribly fascinating has been this tale of murderous Jack that criminologists, novelists, playwrights, tea-leaf readers, clairvoyants, lawyers and doctors have continued their interest unabated. More than 100 books, ten movies and several operas have been produced about the Ripper. One novel, *The Lodger,* published in 1913, has passed through 31 editions, been translated into 18 languages and been filmed five times.

When the murders began, Queen Victoria, the black-bonneted Widow of Windsor, had been on her throne 51 years. The British Empire stretched virtually from pole to pole; and London, its capital, with a population of four million, was like no other place on earth. In the financial center, bankers financed railways in South America, gold mines in Africa, ranches in America. Along the Strand and the Haymarket, by night, gaslights glinted yellowly on the top hats of swells and on the diamonds of their ladies.

But in the crowded East End of Whitechapel and Commercial Road, there existed such poverty, vice and depravity that Victorian London was known as the wickedest place on earth. This crowded half mile, filled with cheap public houses, brothels, streetwalkers and thieves, was the slaughterhouse of Jack the Ripper.

Jack's first victim was Mary Anne "Polly" Nicholls. Driven by a taste for drink and a desire to kick up her heels, Polly had left her husband and five children to hang around Whitechapel bars. At 42, Polly was pretty no more, and on the night in question had been turned away by a lodging house because she lacked a fourpence to pay.

She was leaning against a lamppost at the corner of a drab, rundown street looking for a client when Jack the Ripper came out of the shadows. There was a whispered conversation. Then Polly and shadowy Jack left the lighted street for a dark side street. Suddenly, instead of the soft embrace of love, a hand was clamped over her mouth so that she could not cry out. Then a brutal slash across her throat, and she was lowered to the pavement, where silent Jack lifted her skirt and slashed her abdomen. Then he crept away into the night. It was the beginning of a pattern Jack was to follow for ten horror-filled weeks.

He struck again only eight days later. His victim was Annie Chapman, a 47-year-old widow who had fallen on hard times and was now a gin-sodden tart. Annie's body, still warm, was found about 6 a.m. in a back yard, with her throat cut so completely that her head was almost severed from her neck, and her womb, ovaries and one kidney removed. Under a water tap nearby was found a leather apron, of a kind worn by shoemakers and slaughterhouse workers—possibly worn by Jack to protect him from his victim's spurting blood.

While violence was commonplace in Whitechapel, the savagery of the crimes and the complete lack of evidence brought shudders and dread to all London. Even in the fashionable West End, where the Ripper never struck, women refused to post letters after dark. In the teeming East End, the now-empty pubs began going bankrupt.

The police sent extra men into the area, and local people formed the Whitechapel Vigilance Committee, offering a reward for information leading to the killer. Queen Victoria—aware of the fall of the smallest sparrow in her Empire—sent word to her Prime Minister, Lord Salisbury, that her police were to find this murderer or feel her righteous wrath.

Then, in late September, the killer acquired a name. A letter in a plain envelope arrived at the office of the Central News Agency, which supplied news to papers throughout the British Empire. It said in part, "I am down on whores, and I shan't quit ripping them until I do get buckled." It was signed, "Jack the Ripper."

By this time, confusion reigned at Scotland Yard. Policemen disguised as women of easy virtue roamed the Whitechapel streets as decoys. Students from Oxford and Cambridge doing social work in the East End organized patrols and joined in the hunt. A number of them were followed by the police as suspects and some disguised policemen were physically set upon by Whitechapel natives as Peeping Toms or worse. But no one found any clues.

In an attempt to be scientific, the police pried open Annie Chapman's dead eyes and photographed them, in the hope that the retinas had retained an image of the last thing she saw. But no images were found. Two bloodhounds, Burgho and Barnaby, were considered for use in the case. At a special trial with policemen serving as quarry, the hounds sniffed with their gigantic noses, lifted their great muzzles to the sky, bayed, and plunged off after innocent strangers. At another trial, on Tooting Common in southwest London, they got lost in the fog, and police stations were notified to watch out for them. The hunt for the Ripper continued without their aid.

On the morning of September 30, the Ripper struck twice more. His first victim was "Long Liz" Stride, a tall, gangling prostitute. A peddler found her at 1 a.m. when he drove his horse and cart into the back yard of the International Workers' Educational Club in Berner Street. She was still bleeding from the slash of the killer's knife.

Thirty minutes later the Ripper struck again, at Catherine Eddowes. She had spent the early part of the evening drinking and had been taken by the police to the station house at Bishopsgate to sober up. It was Saturday night, and the cells filled quickly with drunks. Word was sent to turn loose the most sober. Catherine was one of those released.

She wandered into the streets at 1 a.m. and, somewhere in her unsteady path from the police station to Mitre Square, she met Jack. At 1:45 a.m., a police constable, walking his beat, found Catherine's body. Her face had been badly mutilated, her throat had been cut, and the left kidney and most of her entrails had been removed and carried away. Jack the Ripper had committed both crimes within easy sight and sound of his pursuers, then had vanished without trace.

Before the news had become public, the Ripper wrote again to the Central News Agency. His postcard advised that he had been interrupted during the first "event" and had gone on to the second, to try to fulfill the promise made in an earlier letter to "clip the lady's ears off and send to police officers." The card was written in red ink.

The double murder touched off a protest by not only the East Enders—including 4000 women who sent a petition to the Queen—but by others as well. The terrible conditions of the poor and the total failure of the police nearly brought down the government. The Queen, in a rage, sent a letter to the Home Secretary suggesting that he get moving or else. Whitechapel came alive with vigilantes and police. Thousands of letters flooded into Scotland Yard from hoaxers claiming to be Jack.

For almost six weeks Jack the Ripper was quiet. But he was not yet finished. November 9 was foggy and damp, and at 10:45 a.m. a rent collector knocked at the door of No. 13 Miller's Court, a miserable rooming house where Mary Jeanette Kelly, a 24-year-old prostitute, headquartered. When there was no answer, the rent collector, accustomed to tenants' dodges, went to a broken side window, pushed aside the greasy curtain and peered in. What he saw sent him screaming for the police. The remains of Mary Kelly lay on her bed. Her head had been almost severed from her body. Her heart had been placed on her pillow and her entrails draped over a picture frame.

With Mary Kelly's death, the killings ascribed to Jack the Ripper came to an end. And the mystery about his identity began to assume the proportions which were to turn the case into the greatest murder mystery of all time.

At the start, it was assumed that the sinister Jack was one of Whitechapel's butchers or slaughterhouse workers who knew the district well, or someone who had a hiding place where he could change from his bloodstained clothing quickly. A local shoemaker named Pizer was apprehended in connection with the murder of Annie Chapman, but though he owned many sharp knives, he also had an airtight alibi for the time of the murder.

Later it was thought that Jack was a silk-hatted toff from a fashionable precinct of London, and probably a doctor. A mysterious Harley Street surgeon was hinted at—whose son had contracted venereal disease from a prostitute and who was now wreaking his revenge.

Among the hundreds of other suspects, then or later, have been the Duke of Clarence, grandson of Queen Victoria; the cousin of novelist Virginia Woolf; an insane young lawyer who committed suicide; Dr. Neill Cream, the poisoner who died on the gallows in Chicago in 1892 and whose last words cut short by the rope were, "I am Jack—"; a terrible-tempered Polish barber who was hanged after poisoning his wives; members of the Czarist secret police sent to kill women to embarrass Scotland Yard. To date, every theory advanced has been shown to have one or more fatal flaws which eliminate it from serious consideration.

Whether or not the terrible Ripper's identity is ever established, certain things are known about him: none of his victims were raped, he killed about the time of the new moon, he had a degree of surgical or butchering skill, and all his victims were prostitutes. And all were killed between midnight and 5 a.m., within a quarter-mile area packed with thousands of prospective witnesses.

Among the puzzles which still surround the case, none is more intriguing than how the maniacal killer could have performed his dark deeds and vanished without trace after each crime. Curiously enough, it was Sir Arthur Conan Doyle, the creator of Jack's literary contemporary, Sherlock Holmes, who offered the most reasonable solution. "The Ripper," said Sir Arthur, "made his escapes disguised as a woman." But again there is no fact to back up this theory.

Close Encounter
of Flight 101

by Larry Engelmann

SUNDAY MORNING, August 16, 1942. Riccardo Capovilla was on a beach near San Francisco when he saw, only 49 feet from the water's edge, an airship—a blimp, dragging a long rope along the top of the water. The propellers were not turning. No crew was in sight.

Whose airship? American? Japanese? The ship reached the shoreline, made a little turn in the breeze, and Capovilla saw U.S. NAVY L-8. But why was the airship landing here? And its shape was not right. There was a crease across its middle—from loss of pressure—as if some giant had straddled it and broken its back.

The single landing wheel dragged across the sand, then the craft rose gently and moved up along high ground and across a road. The gondola scraped, a depth charge broke loose and rolled down an embankment. Free of this weight, the ship jumped quickly to 98 feet and glided on inland, out of Capovilla's sight. He hurried to phone the police.

MRS. HORACE APPLETON was in her kitchen in the San Francisco suburb of Daly City when she heard what sounded like heavy chains dragging across the roof. The room darkened and she heard the sound of escaping gas. The sky out the window was filled with a big airship. As she watched it fall into the street in front of the home of William Morris, a power line broke, sending arcs of lightning into the air. The helium bag draped itself lazily over Morris's 1928 Dodge.

Firemen, policemen and air-raid wardens formed a cordon to hold back a growing crowd, then navy and army units armed with rifles and bayonets took over. To prevent the blimp from rising again, firemen tore large wounds in its gas-bag. Fireman Thomas O'Brien climbed into the Gondola. It was empty. The—door was latched open—*odd,* he thought—and the safety bar to block the open doorway was not in place. A navy officer's cap lay on the instrument panel. The radio was on and working, and a microphone attached to an outside speaker system dangled through the doorway. The engine ignition switches were on, the gasoline fuel lines open, and there was fuel in the tanks.

Had the engines stalled? Why? Parachutes and a rubber life raft were in place. There was nothing broken or spilled, nothing out of place. No blood, no bullet holes, no smell of gunpowder from the machine gun. Nothing. Behind one seat was the pilot's heavily weighted and locked briefcase containing classified orders.

A search by sea and air turned up no trace of the missing crew. It was as if they had been snatched without warning from their airship while it was in flight. But how? And by whom? And for what reason? To this very day, the riddle remains unsolved.

THE airship L-8 was a part of a blimp patrol inaugurated in March 1942 as a security net for the California coast, to warn of Japanese attack and to spot and sink Japanese submarines. It had been instituted in the midst of nearly hysterical fears of a Japanese invasion.

In January, the scow *Tahoe* had rammed an enemy submarine in broad daylight off the Farallons just outside San Francisco's Golden Gate. On that same day, a submarine put a shell through the oil tanker *Agwiworld* off the coast at Santa Cruz. On February 23, a Japanese submarine surfaced in the Santa Barbara Channel, cruised in close to shore and fired more than 30 shells. And at 3 a.m. February 25, antiaircraft batteries blazed away as unidentified aircraft were reported over Los Angeles. As a result of all this, the blimp patrol was started as an early warning and defense system.

The two-engined L-8 belonged to Squadron 32, which patrolled a 50 mile radius from the Golden Gate Bridge. She was 50 yards long with a maximum diameter of 15 yards and a helium content of 4524 cubic yards. Her armament consisted of two depth bombs and a 30-caliber machine gun. She flew from the Golden Gate to the Farallons, then to Point Reyes and along the coast back to the Bridge, repeating this patrol as often as possible on her 150 gallon fuel capacity.

On August 16, shortly before 6 a.m., a ground crewman at the Treasure Island base started the L-8's engines. For 15 minutes he listened and checked and rechecked her controls. Aviation Machinist's Mate James Riley Hill arrived soon after and made some preflight log entries. Moments later, Lt. DeWitt Cody climbed aboard, followed by Ensign Charles Ellis Adams. Cody, 27, one of the most capable pilots in the command, had 800 hours flying time in nonrigid airships. Adams, 37, commissioned only the previous day after 20 years as an enlisted man, had flown in every type of naval aircraft and had logged nearly 2300 hours.

The L-8, identified this day as Flight 101, was towed onto the short runway. Cody placed his hat on the instrument panel and his briefcase behind his seat. He gunned the engines, then turned to Hill and without explanation ordered him from the ship. The machinist's mate opened the door, jumped to the runway and closed the door behind him. He watched the L-8 taxi for about 147 yards before lifting off and heading toward the Golden Gate Bridge.

At 7:38 a.m., Flight 101 radioed Treasure Island: "Position four miles east of Farallons—stand by." Four minutes later: "Am investigating suspicious oil slick—stand by." That was Flight 101's last message.

Just before that, Master A.A. Backman in the S.S. *Daisy Gray* saw two areas of smoke and some flames on the surface directly below the blimp. He concluded she had dropped signals. At 7:42 (as Flight 101 was transmitting her final signal), a lookout in the steamship *Albert Galatin,* several kilometers astern of *Daisy Gray,* saw the blimp drop a smoke bomb, the signal for *submarine below me.* Capt. Cyrus Brown sounded a general alarm, then watched the L-8 slowly descend to within 10 yards of the water. He saw nothing in the sea beneath the blimp except the smoke signals, and concluded she had spotted a whale and was carrying out a practice maneuver. The L-8 pulled up to about 50 yards, stabilized, circled the smoke signals and climbed slowly into cloud.

Shortly before 11 a.m., Flight 101 was spotted by the pilot of a Pan American Clipper about 3 miles off the Golden Gate Bridge. She was at about 33 yards, fully inflated and under control. The pilot of an army P-38 saw her at about the same time and discerned nothing unusual. A few minutes later as a navy patrol plane flew over the cloud at about 654 yards, the L-8 loomed up close to the right. The airship floated alongside the plane for a moment, then dropped back into the cloud.

The next reported sighting was Riccardo Capovilla's.

THE navy found no explanation for Flight 101's engines having stopped. As for the door: it was possible the men had latched it open, for how could it have been opened from the outside? The only unusual evidence aboard was the fact that the amplifier for the outside speaker had been switched to "stand by." Cody and Adams either had spoken with someone outside or were preparing to speak with someone outside. But to whom? And where? In the water? On the beach? In the clouds?

There was a remote possibility that both men had fallen out the open door. Yet there was neither a strong wind nor a rough sea that day. Neither man was seen to fall. Neither was spotted in the water or washed ashore. One year later, Cody and Adams were officially presumed dead. How they died is a mystery after nearly 40 years.

FILM writer-director Steven Spielberg, in *Close Encounters of the Third Kind,* had mysteries like that of Flight 101 in mind when he portrayed the first landing of an alien spacecraft on earth. When the door of the craft opened, a group of dazed men slowly walked out. "They were dressed in naval flak jackets of the '40s," Spielberg wrote. "They were all very young and several of them were holding leather helmets and flight goggles in their hands."

Unnatural Death

A Bullet From Nowhere

by Albert A. Seedman and Peter Hellman

IT IS 8:40 on Friday morning, July 8, 1967: a dazzler of a day in Brooklyn—not a cloud in the sky, just a hint of breeze blowing in from Sheepshead Bay, traffic moving well on the Belt Parkway toward Manhattan. For several minutes now, Detective Lieutenant Vito DeSiero, on his way to work on Staten Island, has been following a bright-yellow Camaro sports car driven by a teen-age girl. He likes watching the way the soft air off the bay swirls her blond hair.

As they pass a spot called Plum Beach, the girl begins to drift from the passing lane toward the center lane. She keeps drifting to the right, and DeSiero assumes she'll get off at the next exit. Except that she keeps drifting . . . drifting . . . and suddenly with a crackle and splinter she is sideswiping the bushes at the edge of the parkway. The bumper bashes in, the hood crumples. In a tangle of foliage and a hiss of steam, the Camaro stops.

DeSiero is on the scene in seconds. The girl's head is bowed; she is moaning. He raises her head. Though her eyes are open, the eyeballs are rolled back. DeSiero knows, from too much experience, that it is useless to talk to her. Her license reveals she is Nancy McEwen, 17. Nothing in her wallet to warn of epileptic seizures, or diabetic collapse. Her body is unmarked. What has happened to her?

DeSiero calls for an ambulance, and the girl is taken to

Coney Island Hospital. There the doctors try everything—electrical stimulation, adrenalin injections, manual heart massage. Nothing works. At 11:15, Nancy McEwen is declared dead. And only then do the doctors discover, hidden by the long hair on the left side of her head, a small, bloodless bullet hole.

At the same hour, with the sun hot now on the Belt Parkway, an unmarked black Ford sedan pulls up to the scene of the accident. Albert Seedman, puffing his second cigar of the morning, gets out of the back seat and strolls over to the Camaro. He is a broad-shouldered man of 48, hair silvery-gray and lightly oiled, lips well-sculpted and slightly downturned, eyes cold-green. The cops respectfully make way for the unsmiling commander of all Brooklyn South detectives.

Lt. Bernie Jacobs, commander of the local 61st Detective Squad, quickly explained to Seedman the little they knew about Nancy McEwen. She had been on her way to her summer job at her father's construction firm in Brooklyn. Except for what DeSiero saw as she passed Plum Beach that morning, what happened to her was a mystery.

"Jeez," said Jacobs, shaking his head, "who would want to shoot a sweet young kid like that?"

"Nobody," snapped Seedman. "At 45 m.p.h., nobody—not even the best marksman in the world—could make such a perfect head shot. He would have to fire from a car pulling alongside at the same speed—but Vito would have seen that. This thing had to be a crazy, one-in-a-trillion, pure fluke." He stared at the Camaro. "Did anyone roll the windows up or down?"

"No, Chief," answered Jacobs. "That's the way it was— just the left rear window open."

Since the glass in all other windows was intact, the left rear window was the only possible source of the bullet. So it must have been shot from somewhere behind the Camaro on the side of the parkway facing Sheepshead Bay. It could have come from the reeds and low dunes that sloped down to Plum Beach, or from the public bathhouse 200 yards back from the highway, or from the parking lot alongside the eastbound lanes. The shot might also have been fired from a boat on the bay. Or even from any of the three 28-story steel apartment-tower skeletons two miles across the bay.

Seedman ordered Emergency Service and Ballistics units to comb the beach and dunes for the shell casing. He knew it was an awful place to look for anything so small, but if they could find the casing, it would tell them where the shot had come from. "Tell those guys to bring their swim trunks," said Seedman. "Losing their weekend won't seem so bad if they can take a few dips."

All during the long daylight hours of the weekend, search teams scoured the sand at Plum Beach. They found no shell casing. On Monday morning Seedman called in a special Army Ordnance team from Fort Monmouth, N.J., to work with metal detectors. Still nothing. As the sun went down on Monday evening, a tired, disgusted Seedman stood on the beach scanning the marshy spur of dunes to the east, Fort Tilden and the towers of Breezy Point across the bay. "That bullet could have come from so many places besides this beach you can't even count them all," he said to Lieutenant Jacobs.

On Tuesday morning, Seedman sent detectives to Nancy McEwen's Requiem Mass in the hope that the man who fired the shot would turn up. One nervous young man nobody knew did take off fast after the service, but detectives found he was just a school chum of Nancy's in a hurry to get back to his office. A dozen citizens called the police that same day to say they also had been shot at as they drove to work on the Belt Parkway. But the "sniper" turned out to be a mowing machine that had been pelting stones from its whirring blades.

On Tuesday, too, the FBI returned a report on the death bullet. It had been fired from an Enfield .303, a model manufactured in England about 1940 on an around-the-clock production schedule. *Millions* of the rifles were still in circulation.

Five days of work by dozens of detectives, and Seedman was still nowhere. His men had turned up no gun dealer who had recently sold an Enfield .303. They had covered all the marinas, climbed the skeletons at Breezy Point, crawled around the dunes and marshes at Plum Beach, called in the Army, checked out every wild tip that came in on the "hot line"—and still had no idea who had shot Nancy McEwen, or why, or even where the bullet had come from.

Seedman was well aware how much taxpayers' money had gone into the case so far with no results. But he was not ready to quit trying to find the person who killed Nancy McEwen. Not quite yet.

"We're going to make a canvass," he announced to his men. "Starting tomorrow morning, we're going to knock on every door in Brooklyn until we find the guy who has that Enfield. He isn't talking now, but when a detective comes calling he's going to figure we've traced the gun to him somehow. And then he'll come clean."

The detectives looked at one another. Covering just a single block of the city can be time-consuming, but Seedman was talking about a borough of three million people! It would take longer than their lifetimes. "You've got to be kidding, Chief," Jacobs said. "Where would we start?"

A large map of Brooklyn was pinned to the office wall. Seedman ran his finger slowly up and down the lower half of the borough. Suddenly, the finger stopped. "Start . . . right . . . *here*."

Jacobs marked the block: Knapp Street north of the Belt Parkway, about a mile in front of where the Camaro had run off the road. It was not a direction from which the bullet could have come. Why had Seedman's finger jabbed that particular spot? The Chief himself could not explain, then or later.

The next morning two detectives began working the block on Knapp Street. The third place they came to was a Mobil station. In the office they found the proprietor, a chunky man of 46 named Theodore DeLisi, working over his bills.

"Do you own a rifle?" the detectives asked.

"Oh, I have one down in my boat, locked away."

"What kind?"

"It's . . . an Enfield," DeLisi said, his eyes glued to his bills. "One of those British jobs."

DeLisi felt the silence, and looked up in dread.

"That girl, she was killed by a .22 rifle, right? That's what I read in the paper. Please tell me she got it from a .22 . . ."

This is the story that Theodore DeLisi told during seven hours of questioning on Wednesday. Two weeks earlier, at the end of June, he had gone out in his boat *Luau* to fish for bluefish off Rockaway Beach. The blues were there, but so were sharks, and they scared the blues away. Frustrated, DeLisi remembered that when he and two other men had bought the *Luau* a few years back, a rifle had been thrown into the deal— just the thing to deal with those sharks. On his return, DeLisi picked up the gun from the partner who had been keeping it.

July 8 was a great day for fishing. No clouds, just a hint of wind on Rockaway Inlet. As he chugged by buoy No. 7 in the channel to the ocean, DeLisi reached for the Enfield. "Might as well see if the damn thing works," he said. He saw a beer can bobbing near the buoy. He took aim, and hit the can with his first shot. Pleased, he raised the rifle and fired one more shot before putting out to the open sea.

The second bullet missed the can, smacking the water beyond it at a shallow angle. To a bullet at that speed, the surface of the water is as hard as a sheet of steel. It richocheted with a pop and headed north across Rockaway Inlet. It whistled along at almost four feet over the blue, flat water, and remained at that height as it crossed the sand, the dunes and the reeds of Plum Beach. Far ahead of the sound of its own report, it sped across the parking lot and the eastbound lanes of the parkway, and just cleared the fence divider on the median strip. As it approached the yellow Camaro—nearly a mile from the *Luau*—the bullet had begun to lose momentum. Had the rear left window of the car been closed, it would probably have glanced off. As it was, the bullet had just enough force to penetrate behind the left ear of Nancy McEwen.

ON July 18, 1967, in Brooklyn Criminal Court, Theodore DeLisi was charged with the homicide of Nancy McEwen and with discharging a rifle within city limits. The homicide charge was later dropped, and DeLisi was fined $100 on the lesser charge. Incredibly, it turned out that he and the dead girl were acquainted, and had once been neighbors in northern Queens.

Detectives still talk about the Belt Parkway Case because of its three amazing coincidences. The first, obviously, was that after traversing a mile-long sweep of water and sand, the bullet had found the one place where it could do fatal damage. The second was that out of the city's millions, the families of shooter and victim knew each other. But what appeared to be the greatest coincidence of all was not dismissed as such by the detectives. In the 240 square miles of the borough, their Chief had put his finger precisely on the one block where the Belt Parkway Case could be closed. His men had seen it happen too many times to call it anything but a particularly mysterious example of Albert Seedman's very special instinct.

The City That Died of Fear

by Albert Q. Maisel

HIGH IN the mountains of eastern Arizona archeologists have partly uncovered one of the greatest of all Indian pueblos, a city of more than 5000 souls that was founded about the time of Christ. Along with multi-room dwellings, ceremonial rooms and storehouses, magnificent pottery and well-preserved skeletons, the scientists have unearthed one of the most perplexing mysteries of all time.

For the city of Point-of-Pines died an unnatural death.

One night—a hundred years before Columbus—its people apparently went to sleep as usual. Next day every man, woman and child fled, leaving all their treasures where they lay— jewelry, stone axes, precious arrowheads and children's toys. In their mad haste they even left cook pots steaming on their hearth fires.

And they never returned.

Whatever it was that drove them off, their city stood unharmed until time caved it into ruin, and the winds drifted the earth into vast, gentle mounds that remained inviolate for nearly 600 years.

In the mid-1940s, under the guidance of Professor Emil W. Haury of the University of Arizona and Curator E. B. Sayles of the Arizona State Museum, graduate students and visiting scientists first dug downward through the centuries to trace the record of a civilization's gradual rise and sudden fall.

This much is now certain: these people were no longer nomads. The miracle plant, corn, had freed them from a life of wandering. In their first crude houses—round holes four or five feet deep, hooded over with wattles and mud—were storage bins filled with precious grain which the women ground by laboriously rubbing stone manos against hollowed-out lava blocks.

Then from out of the North came new settlers, known to us. as the Anasazi, the Navajo name for "the ancient ones." They peacefully built their stone pueblos alongside the primitive huts of the original inhabitants. As the centuries ticked slowly by they established quarries and with stone axes squared the volcanic rocks, then hauled the heavy blocks laboriously down the slopes to their growing city. To save the labor of building new four-walled houses, they tacked additions onto their central structures—and even raised second and third stories—until their largest pueblo contained more than 800 rooms on its ground floor alone. It stretched for nearly a quarter of a mile.

To feed their growing numbers, the Anasazi developed an amazing gift for engineering. Their 6000-foot plateau was semi-arid. Melting snows and summer showers ran off in flash floods that left only parched soil. With uncanny judgment the Anasazi traced contour lines, laid down miles of stone retaining walls and trapped the floods upon thousands of new leveled terraces. It must have taken them a hundred years or more for they had not even a single beast of burden. But gradually they had prospered, the corn and beans grew high and their storerooms were guarantees against starvation through the winters.

All this the archeologists can deduce. They know that time brought with it art, for the painting of the deeper levels is primitive and crude, while that of the later years, the golden years from 1000–1200 A.D., is intricately decorated polychrome in a tremendous range of shapes and designs.

Point-of-Pines must have been a trading center for a score of Indian civilizations in a 500-mile circle, as many of the pottery remnants are made of clays not found on a plateau or bear designs and pigments originating hundreds of miles away. From the evidence, the men of Point-of-Pines journeyed as far as Chihuahua in Mexico, to the Rio Grande country and into the lands of the desert Indians where Phoenix and Tucson now stand.

Pottery was not the only thing traded. After the crops were gathered and before the deep snows came, the men journeyed down to the lower Gila country, their backs bent under bales of animal skins. They returned with cotton from the hot lowlands. Combining cotton with yucca fibers, the women fashioned a sturdy, supple cloth.

Occasionally the men made even longer journeys. The Anasazi women wore beautiful jewelry fashioned from abalone shells that could have come only from the Pacific, nearly 700 miles away. Their long black hair they swept up into buns held in place by deer-bone hairpins. Hematite, the red oxide of iron, they particularly prized as rouge, carefully preserving little cakes of it in tiny pots which Haury's students have uncovered intact after more than 500 years.

Point-of-Pines architects planned and constructed large kivas (ceremonial rooms), one with a floor area of more than 300 square feet where 500 men could sit—or rather, squat. There were many smaller kivas, too, dug partly into the ground and entered by a ladder from a hole in the roof. These underground, windowless rooms posed a difficult ventilation problem. Anasazi engineers solved it by digging a horizontal tunnel through one wall and a vertical shaft to the surface. Hot air and smoke from the hearth immediately below the central entrance hole rose through ports in the roof, to be replaced by fresh air which came sweeping in through the side-wall tunnel.

Life was good at Point-of-Pines—so good that it is hard to imagine why these people ever left their plateau paradise. The archeologists can tell us for certain that Point-of-Pines did not fall victim to the Apaches as did other pueblos of the Southwest. Wherever these fierce nomads raided, the charred remnants of burning roof beams fell over the bodies of their slaughtered victims. There is nothing like that at Point-of-Pines.

Starvation can be ruled out, too. Haury and Sayles have found charred corn and beans in many of the excavated rooms.

Was it a plague that drove them off? If this were true one would expect to find the bodies of the dying abandoned like the fires and kitchen tools. No such bodies have been found.

How then can the exodus be explained? Haury and Sayles have a theory which starts with a fact firmly established by the 2000-year tree-ring chronology developed by their associate, Dr. A.E. Douglass. The rings of trees are the history of rainfall. And Dr. Douglass's records, compiled from hundreds of tree samples, show that a great drought devastated the entire Southwest for 23 years from 1276 to 1299.

This was at least 100 years before the panic at Point-of-Pines. Yet there are many signs that the drought marked the end of that city's golden age. Undoubtedly the terraced fields and storehouses filled with grain helped sustain the tribe for years. Also, they dug wells of a special type found only in one other spot on earth, far-off Mesopotamia. These wells were in the form of wide, inverted cones—dug down to uncover deep-lying water. Into these walk-in wells the inhabitants must have marched every day under a blazing, rainless sky, and carried from them millions of pots of precious fluid to the parched terraces to save their corn.

As the years of drought stretched into decades, the Anasazi had to dig their wells deeper and deeper, until the footsteps of the patient water carriers wound three complete circles down the ramps to the tiny pools at the bottom.

The wells saved them, and at length the rains returned. But the long succession of evil years must have burned the heart out of this brave people. From 1300 onward, their once flourishing culture declined. Those who survived, stunted and weakened by two lean decades, had to support all too many people aged before their time by years of extra toil.

There was no time, after the drought, for the luxury labors of jewel carving and pottery painting. Even the dead could no longer be honored as in the golden days when men had been buried with their dogs, their prize turkeys, their axes and tools. Burials became mere chuckaways, with bodies thrown into abandoned rooms along with broken pottery and other trash.

The years of the Anasazi misery dragged on; their unbalanced economy just couldn't, it seemed, be restored. At council meetings in the Great Kiva there must have been, increasingly, suggestions that they flee the evils that beset them.

Only a spark was needed to light the psychological tinder. Possibly that spark was the word "Apache." In 1385 these marauders burned and sacked the Gila Pueblo only 100 miles away. This news may have been enough to tip the scales for flight.

Where did the Anasazi go? The Hopi and Zuni people, 200 miles to the north, were also Anasazi, closely related to the inhabitants of Point-of-Pines. The modern Hopi have no legends of a welcome for their blood brothers. But it is known that the Zuni villages became larger at the end of the 14th century. The rest is mystery.

If the mystery of Point-of-Pines could be deciphered, it might prove of inestimable value to the Southwest. For today the agricultural economy of this region is again precarious. Tucson and Phoenix are burgeoning into the modern equivalent of Point-of-Pines' golden years, and have lowered the water table significantly. Buried in the failure of Point-of-Pines may lie an ancient warning to modern man, whose continued existence in this beautiful land of sun is also threatened by drought.

Killers of the Sea

by Joy Williams

Q. What did you hear?
A. I heard an awful splash that sounded like an explosion.
Q. What did you see?
A. I saw a swimmer trying to get away from a shark, swimming with his arms. (Extract of evidence re the death of Brian Derry, Safety Bay, Tasmania, 1959.)

WHEN men catch sharks, they do not simply kill them, they mutilate them as though in the grip of an ancient rite. They hatchet fins, chop out jaws, slit open bellies. Men hate sharks. They hate them a *lot*. But the reality of the creature's existence cannot truly be confronted. The shark is deft and original and very ancient. Dead or alive, it inhabits impossible depths and will inhabit them forever.

On May 7, 1959, at about 5:45 p.m., the deceased and a friend, Shirley O'Neill, were swimming at Bakers Beach, off the Golden Gate, and were about 30 yards from shore, swimming parallel to each other and talking back and forth, when suddenly Miss O'Neill saw the deceased disappear under the water, and the tail of a large fish shoot out of the water nearby.

Deceased then rose to the surface. Miss O'Neill started for shore and then, seeing that the deceased was in obvious distress, returned to assist deceased back to shore. When they arrived ashore, it was noted that deceased was suffering from partial amputation of the left shoulder and arm, multiple lacerations of left chest and multiple deep lacerations of right shoulder, arm and chest. Authorities were notified. (History taken from Coroner's Register re the death of Albert Kogler in California.)

SHARKS attack approximately 50 to 60 people a year. That's not many. Nevertheless, the thought of a big fish lunching on a fated bather is known to create concern out of all proportion to the amount of injury or loss of life incurred statistically. Somewhere or other, there's a Bronze Whaler or a Grey Nurse or a White Death out to do the purely unspeakable. Rolling and trimming, balancing and pivoting, flying with baseball eyes through the sea, without malice or immoral intent, a percentage of sharks bite a percentage of people. The chosen can be a silver-suited diver or a black pearler or a little boy in a T-shirt or a woman bathing with her gentleman friend after lunch.

At the time of the incident, all the spear fishermen (Wilson, Hitt, Kirkman, Churchill and Skinner) were similarly equipped, and Graeme Hitt was wearing a ¼-inch wet suit with blue fins, black face mask, blue snorkel with white top and brown leather glove on left hand. He was carrying a green spear gun. There is no tangible reason why Graeme Hitt was attacked in preference to the other men except that he was the person swimming on the surface nearest to where the shark appeared. (Fatal. Aramoana, Otago Harbour, New Zealand, 1968.)

SHARKS can attack anybody. They just don't seem to care. It's man who persists in believing there are common factors associated with the elected. Bathing-suit color or frame of mind or torn hangnail or mucky water or whatever. Avoid the common factor, man thinks, and you'll live to leave the sea.

THE pressure exerted by the jaws of a typical eight-foot shark is three metric tons a square centimeter.

SHARKS are not deterred consistently by anything. Most precautions are too preliminary to be helpful (don't swim alone or at night or in bloody water or in water where sharks have been sighted) or too much after the fact (all efforts should be made to control hemorrhage as quickly as possible). There are dozens of actions one *might* take. Remain calm; bop the fish smartly on the snout; leave the water as unobtrusively as possible. Most swimmers believe that splashing or clapping is a deterrent, although evidence shows that splashing or thrashing or even the tremors caused by relativley smooth swimming are what attract the shark to the area in the first place.

Nothing works constantly, that's all. There is no universally correct action to take in case of shark attack.

THE International Shark Attack File, begun in 1959, is presently contained in 11 large filing drawers in the National Underwater Accident Data Center at the University of Rhode Island in Kingston. There are over 2000 cases on record, which represent only a portion of the attacks which have actually occurred.

The files are in folders; red plastic inserts on the far right of a folder indicate fatal encounters; clear ones on the far left denote non-fatal ones. Staggered in between are markers which are green (provoked or doubtful attacks), yellow (air-sea disasters), and blue (boats). It all has an obsessive, commanding neatness about it, and people always seem impressed when they open a drawer and see what appears to be a vast amount of highly organized information.

All of this "evidence" was gathered together in a project contracted between the U.S. Navy and the Smithsonian Institution, which believed that we have enough troubles in this life without having to worry about being eaten by a fish. Information was accumulated in order to become data which would then be fed into a "retrieval system." There were facts and now there were going to be questions and answers. How can one keep from being in the right place at the right time? What were these sharks thinking of? Conclusions would be reached.

More than $100,000 has been spent in establishing and maintaining the Shark Attack File over the years, and there is so much of everything—medical and scientific reports, newspaper clippings, morgue photographs, military reports, first-person accounts, slides, tapes—that one cannot be blamed for being confident that conclusions would be reached.

In two Australian attacks the victims were swimming to retrieve tennis balls thrown into the water.

Case No. 1017: The shark attacked Mr. Hoogvorst at 9 a.m. when the tide was ebbing. The victim was a strong swimmer and accustomed to swimming far out to sea. Mr. Hoogvorst had an open wound caused by a blister on the heel of his right foot. Mr. Hoogvorst was unemployed. Hr. Hoogvorst was wearing a royal-blue bathing costume.

Case No. 637: Two fishermen battled with an eight-foot shark which jumped into their 14-foot boat. Richard Crew, 52, said the shark leaped straight at him. "The shark must have been attracted or infuriated by my green yachting jacket," Crew said.

Case No. 236: The movements of the shark were at all times deliberate and leisurely. Neither during the initial strike nor while making subsequent strikes nor while convoying the swimmers toward shore did its speed impress any observer. It made no abrupt lunges and never seemed to be exerting itself. Wilson was struck four times by the shark, at least twice while he was being rescued and closely surrounded by five swimmers. (Fatal. Imperial Beach, California, 1950.)

THIRTY-FIVE percent of all people attacked by sharks die. That's a statistic and a discovery of sorts, but its relevance is illusive. There are things which are not being said. It is simply too dreadful. The more detailed the account, the more one becomes aware that there is nothing to be grasped. Despite our painful bondage to fact, we realize that both the form and formality of documentation bring us nothing but emptiness.

The sensory systems of sharks, although beautifully interrelated, nevertheless result in a decidedly limited behavioral repertoire. Once they have initiated a specific pattern of behavior, they are not readily distracted or inhibited. Often they continue to attack their prey despite a variety of normally distracting and noxious stimuli, even including severe bodily crippling.

Such an object! Both primitive and futuristic with its simple core of mystery, with its actions, exact, obsessed and inexplicable . . .

Case No. 1406: The victim endeavored to fight the shark off and bit it on its snout to make it release its grip on his right leg but without effect. A surf-club member first reached the victim, who said, "Help me, please. The shark's still there." The rescuer could not see the shark and did not believe the victim until he tried to drag him ashore. Five other lifesavers then arrived and half pulled and half carried the shark and victim to knee-deep water. The shark was struck with a surfboard but would not release its grip until dragged ashore and its jaws pried open. (Non-fatal attack. Coledale Beach, Australia. 2/26/66.)

SUCH a deep imperviousness to life! Such silence. Such invisibility. As though created instantly, when needed, out of the sea itself. What can be learned from the shark but negation? The facts presented by computer readout of the files' contents are reasonable and of scant help to anyone.

The shark likes blood and fish, but it often attacks man when neither of these excitants is present. In fact, a significant fraction of shark attacks on humans appear to be motivated by factors other than hunger. The shark strikes in the rain and the bright sunshine, off crowded beaches and in rivers 70 miles from the sea. Neither month nor time of day nor condition of sea or sky nor depth of water is applicable to the probability of attack.

THE shark moves boneless from the sea light into the darkness of our worst imaginings. And as the impossible terminus, as the inconceivable hazard, it slips from our dreams into the sea.

Ghosts, Goblins
and Haunted Houses

Adventure at Versailles

by Maurice Shadbolt

ON AUGUST 10, 1901, two middle-aged English spinsters went walking at Versailles in the gardens near the Petit Trianon, where the young Marie Antoinette used to amuse herself. Soon they began suffering inexplicable depression: the trees around them grew flat and lifeless "like a wood worked in tapestry." And suddenly, incredibly—or so they decided later—they went back in time to the 18th century.

Initially, failing to identify the extraordinary nature of their experience, they took what they saw for granted. Finding themselves at the end of a lane among farm buildings, they asked directions of two men in green livery wearing three-cornered hats—gardeners, they thought, since there was a wheelbarrow and spade near by. The men, one old and one young, told the spinsters, in a mechanical way, to go straight on. To the right of the men one of the ladies observed a cottage where a woman and girl in unusual and dated ankle-length dress stood at the doorway.

Following the gardeners' direction, the two spinsters walked on. One of them recalled: "An extraordinary depression had come over me, which, in spite of every effort to shake off, steadily deepened." Remembered her companion: "I began to feel as if I were walking in my sleep: the heavy dreaminess was oppressive."

They encountered a small wood, in which was a circular

kiosk, like a small bandstand. A man sitting nearby in dark cloak and large shady hat turned to look at them—and for the first time the women felt alarm. It wasn't just that the man had a pock-marked and frightening face: "The eerie feeling which had begun in the garden culminated in a definite impression of something uncanny . . . His expression was very evil and yet unseeing."

Then came the sound of running feet, though at first they saw no one. Suddenly a handsome young man in broad-brimmed hat, cloak and buckled shoes appeared almost magically before them, red-faced as though with great exertion. Excitedly he directed them away from the kiosk and the unpleasant-looking man. Before both women could thank him he vanished.

They crossed a rustic bridge over a tiny ravine with thread-like waterfall and found their way into a garden overlooked by a country house. In this garden, insisted one of the women, a fair-haired lady in rather old-fashioned summer dress, with low-cut bodice, sat sketching.

"When we passed close by on her left hand, she turned and looked full at us. It was not a young face, and (though rather pretty) it did not attract me." Her companion, however, saw no lady there at all: she remembered only "drawing my skirt away with a feeling as though someone were near and I had to make room, and then wondering why I did it."

After climbing steps to a terrace in front of the country house, they met a young man leaving a nearby building. He slammed the door loudly behind him, then re-directed them round into the Petit Trianon—and, as it turned out, bewilderingly back into the 20th century.

The two bemused women were in no haste to tell their tale. Indeed, a week passed before they could bring themselves to admit their discomfiting experience to each other; they then agreed that the Petit Trianon must be haunted. So they wrote separate accounts of their walk, which they showed discreetly to friends.

On subsequent visits to Versailles the two women established that the paths on which they walked on August 10, 1901, did not exist in the twentieth century. Buildings they had seen intact and apparently inhabited—like the cottage where the woman and girl evidently dwelt—had vanished. There were no gardeners in green livery and three-cornered hats, no circular kiosk in a little wood, no rustic bridge over a tiny ravine—and no delicate waterfall, either.

A large bush and sweep of gravel now existed where one of the women had seen the sketching lady framed by a garden. The country house was there, but the women couldn't recognize the steps they had taken up to its terrace, and the door the young man had slammed so loudly was bolted, rusted and cobwebbed.

What, then, had happened to the two women on August 10, 1901? Research convinced them that they were reliving the doomed Marie Antoinette's last summer of peace at Versailles by inadvertently entering "an act of the Queen's memory when alive." A long hunt among dusty documents and forgotten maps suggested that many of the features they saw at Versailles *had* existed in the 18th century. More, some of the people they had glimpsed appeared to belong there, too.

That evil-looking, pock-marked man—might he not have been the slightly shady Comte de Vaudreuil, a Creole marked by smallpox, and friend of the Queen? He was cloaked in the fashion of his time. The handsome young running man? Perhaps he was the breathless courtier who brought the Queen news of the mob approaching from Paris. Certainly his buckled shoes were fashionable in the France of 1789. Finally, that sketching lady—surely there was no mistaking her as anyone but Marie Antoinette herself? For she looked remarkably like one of the Queen's contemporary portraits.

This perplexing experience might have been lost forever in the limbo of psychic oddities if the two spinsters had not finally resolved to print in 1911 an account of their visions at Versailles. In fear of mockery, they published their book, *An Adventure,* under pseudonyms.

For years the book—a spectacular success from the start—provided a battleground for the skeptics. When the identity of the women was revealed in 1931, by which time the younger one was dead and the other had just six years to live, it only created more controversy over the book's authenticity: one, Miss Annie Moberly, aged 55 in 1901, was impeccably a bishop's daughter and Principal of St. Hugh's College, Oxford; the other, Miss Eleanor Jourdain, aged 38 on that August day, was likewise daughter of a cleric, and succeeded Miss Moberly as Principal of St. Hugh's. Two more sober and apparently trustworthy women could hardly be imagined.

With the women's names known it became possible to consider *An Adventure* in the light shed by the character of the adventurers themselves. That task was finally performed by the noted author and broadcaster Lucille Iremonger in *The Ghosts of Versailles,* published in 1957 just after the fifth edition and 20th printing of *An Adventure* had put a total of more than 100,000 copies into the hands of a marvelling public.

Skeptical Mrs. Iremonger, though even she couldn't bring herself to damn their story altogether, established conclusively that both women had had psychical experiences before they first visited Versailles. This cut the ground from under many who had always seen the couple as cool, disinterested academics. Mrs. Iremonger also demonstrated that for academics their research had been shoddy. More damning still, doubt was cast on the integrity of Miss Jourdain. It transpired that she had been involved in a petty Oxford scandal.

Even so the spinsters' story, with all the questions it begs, has survived skeptic and cynic. And, since ghosts seldom let a good story down, the hauntings at Versailles appeared to continue after 1901. An English family named Crooke, living there between 1907 and 1909, confirmed the Moberly-Jourdain story: they, too, claimed to have seen that mysterious sketching lady who might have been Marie Antoinette, and a man in 18th century costume.

In 1928 two other Englishwomen of the highest repute—a schoolmistress and her former pupil who later became Lady Hay—had a similar tale to tell of a walk in the Trianon gardens. In 1937, 1938 and 1939, in 1949 and 1955, equally reliable citizens spoke of people in archaic dress, and a Marie Antoinette-like figure, flitting through the grounds of Versailles. Some of these witnesses had read *An Adventure;* some hadn't.

Psychical researchers burrowing into the mystery came up with a piquant finding—that the description of the royal gardens given by Miss Moberly and Miss Jourdain fits more exactly the Versailles of 1770, rather than that of 1789, the date towards which the two women romantically directed their own research.

While no contemporary map shows a kiosk in the Petit Trianon of 1789, a document dated 1776 refers to a "circular pavilion," later demolished, exactly where the spinsters reported one. Foundations of a cottage (also nonexistent on 1789 maps) have been found where Miss Jourdain said she saw such a building. And the women's story, though they themselves were unaware of it, even offers tentative identification of the two royal gardeners, Claude Richard and his son Antoine, who wore green livery in the gardens until 1774.

Connoisseurs of the paranormal, accustomed to viewing *An Adventure* as a continuing and absorbing mystery, were intrigued in 1976 by the announcement of "a rational explanation." It was provided by Dame Joan Evans, the distinguished historian to whom Miss Moberly and Miss Jourdain bequeathed the copyright of their book. Dame Joan now declared herself satisfied that what her two friends had seen was the rehearsal for a *tableau-vivant* by a French nobleman, Comte Robert de Montesquiou, and friends whose enthusiasm for charades in 18th century costume is well authenticated.

This plausible theory has by no means ended the adventure. Among those who challenged Dame Joan's explanation was Lady Gladwyn, wife of a former British ambassador to France. Claiming that Dame Joan had produced no hard evidence, Lady Gladwyn contested her theory point by circumstantial point. She also questioned the likelihood of a rehearsal at the Petit Trianon by the fashionable Comte and his smart friends in the month of August—"a time of year when it was considered social death" to be in or around Paris.

So again the ghosts of the Petit Trianon had refused to be laid. As psychical researcher Andrew MacKenzie said, "The file on the famous Versailles Case is still open."

Our Haunted House on the Hudson

by Helen Herdman Ackley

I SAW our house for the first time on a hot July day. A bedraggled old Victorian, it had stood vacant for seven years. Its waist-high lawn clutched about a sturdy stone foundation; its wood-shingled roof was awry. But as I followed the real-estate agent and my husband, George, into the spacious hall, I knew I was home.

George, already working in New York City, moved into the house as soon as the final papers were signed. My job was to shuttle between our Maryland farm and our new home, closing one while renovating the other. One afternoon the neighborhood children broke up a lively ball game to question me. Yes, we *had* bought the house. Yes, we *did* have children—four—although they wouldn't arrive for another week. When I told them they could look through the house, two of the kids hung back. The others giggled. "They think there's ghosts in there. They're scared. Did you know you bought a haunted house?"

Later in the day, the plumber who was re-creating the water system asked me, "Are you planning to be here long, Mrs. Ackley?"

"Until 4:30, Bob. I have to pick up my husband at five. What's the matter? Have you run into problems?"

Bob hesitated. "It's not that, Mrs. Ackley. I keep hearing footsteps on the stairs and walking around overhead. I must have run up and down those steps six times the other day, and I couldn't find anybody. I'm ready to go now, but I don't want to leave you here alone."

I looked at Bob standing there, young, nearly six feet tall, solidly built. His concern was real.

I managed a smile. "Don't worry, Bob. I might as well get used to being here alone."

That night I told George about the two conversations as we got ready for bed. He nodded his head gravely and pulled up the covers. Sliding in beside him, I realized the hall light was burning. With a groan I started up.

"Where are you going?" George demanded.

"To turn off the light, of course."

"Leave it on."

I looked at him. "Since when have you slept with the light on?"

"Since the first night I moved in here, and I don't want to discuss it. Good night!" He turned over, his back to me.

As I dropped off to sleep, I wondered what it was with these crazy men and this lovely old house. I got nothing but good vibes. So we lived with the footsteps, and I have found it reassuring to have such a vigilant patrolman on duty 24 hours a day. Anyway, all old houses creak.

FOOTSTEPS. A light-fixture cord swaying over the family dinner table on a windless day, then stopped in midswing as if by some unseen hand. French doors suddenly flung open. A casement window gaping. These performances were not given on command, but several friends did see the phenomena. George nailed the casements shut, and Cynthia, our oldest daughter—then 15—quietly closed the French doors when she found them ajar.

GEORGE travels frequently, and at such times I may read into the early morning and even pace about the house with the lights out. One winter night, I stood at the window in the dining room looking out at our view of the Hudson River.

The leaves were gone from the trees, and shore lights shone across the water. The diamond necklace of the Tappan Zee Bridge undulated with light over the still river. As I stood storing the magnificent memory, a chill engulfed my left side. Someone was standing beside me. Very close beside me. Every hair on my neck and scalp stirred as I slowly turned my head. No body stood there, but an entity certainly did occupy that space.

"It's beautiful on the river, isn't it?" I asked aloud. (It isn't that I was calm, but I do react steadily in times of stress.) As I spoke, my hair eased back into place, and I felt no threat in the presence beside me. We stood looking out the window for a few more minutes. Then I turned to leave. My invisible companion turned with me and walked beside me across the room. I hesitated at the door. So did the other.

"Thank you for sharing the view with me. I'm going to bed now. Good night." I walked alone down the hall to my bedroom, quivering, and closed the door behind me. Somehow I got to sleep and slept soundly all night.

CYNTHIA had never been hard to arouse in the mornings, but now she began to get up and dress even before George and I rolled out of bed. "It's spooky, Mother," she explained. "Every morning at exactly the same time my bed starts shaking. And if I don't get up right away, the bed shakes even harder."

Cyn was not scared or even upset. She had just hoped to sleep later during the pending Christmas holiday. The plan we hit upon was not logical, perhaps, but it worked. Cynthia explained the situation to her invisible alarm clock, out loud, before going to bed that night. And during the vacation Cyn slept in every morning.

OVER THE YEARS, we have made many changes in our house. Many times I've been sure that no self-respecting ghost would put up with the hammering, dust and confusion, but odd things continued to occur. The living-room window flew up unexpectedly, startling many a guest. We initiates would nonchalantly murmur, "That's enough, now!" while closing the window. That would usually suffice for the evening. After we had painted the woodwork and the window lock was newly engaged, untoward motion ceased. But sometimes, in the summer, I like to unlock that window and let the ghosts have at it.

ONE DAY I attacked the battleship-gray living room. Paint time was at hand, and I was perched atop an eight-foot stepladder when I felt watching eyes. The feeling was not unfamiliar, but it was still a bit unnerving. I knew George was at work and the kids were in school.

I turned my head. The room was empty. I started working again. But the eerie feeling persisted, so I spoke out loud. "I hope you like the color. Hope you're pleased with what we're doing to the house. It certainly must have been lovely when it was first built."

As I talked I kept painting, but I felt the energy of those eyes, focused on the nape of my neck. I looked over my shoulder again. "He" sat there in midair, smiling at me from in front of the cold fireplace. Hands clasped around his crossed knees, he was nodding and rocking. He faded slowly, still smiling, and was gone. But I knew then that he approved of the work our family had lavished on our mutual home.

What did he look like? He was the most cheerful and solid-looking little person I've ever seen. A cap of white hair framed his round, apple-cheeked face, and there were piercing blue eyes under thick white eyebrows. His light-blue suit was immaculate, the cuffs of the short unbuttoned jacket turned back over ruffles at his wrists. A white ruffled stock showed at his throat. Below breeches cut to his kneecaps he wore white hose and shiny black pumps with buckles.

No, I wasn't drinking that day. No, the paint fumes hadn't got to me. No, I don't know why I saw him then—and have never seen him since. But I do know that he seemed happy to be there, and I was proud to meet him.

CYNTHIA WAS INTERESTED in my description of the gentleman because her shadowy roommate was quite different. On two or three occasions she had seen the outline of a thin hooded figure of medium height, and was quite sure it was a woman.

Through the years, a number of our friends have told us of odd experiences they've had in our home—doors that wouldn't stay closed, voices coming from empty rooms, a sense of being watched or even warned away. But not until my cousin Alfred, his wife, Ingrid, and their daughter came to visit in 1974 did anyone outside our immediate family "meet" one of our ghosts.

At breakfast after their first night with us, Ingrid's hands shook as she held her coffee cup. She had awakened before daylight, she said, aware that someone was walking around in the room. Then, silhouetted against the French doors, she saw the figure of a man dressed in a long jacket of the Revolutionary period. On his head was a curled, white-powdered wig.

He moved to the foot of the bed and sat down with his back toward Ingrid. The mattress gave as if someone had sat down on the edge. Then the figure opened a big book—in midair. The book glowed as if it were lighted from inside. The figure turned the pages one by one as though he were looking for something. Finally he closed it, stood up, and was gone.

THERE ARE always little incidents to mull over in a house like ours. There was the time George's ham sandwich disappeared as he worked. The look on his face was bewilderment and then rage that one of us would eat his hard-earned sandwich. We never really convinced him that we hadn't touched it—although we all concluded, finally, that succulent ham sandwiches must be enticing down through the ages.

OUR GHOSTS have continued to delight us over the years. Just recently, my husband saw a figure in the hall which disappeared as he came up the basement steps. Only the foot was in his line of vision—clad in a soft moccasin-like slipper.

Then there are what we call our gifts from the ghosts. A pair of tiny silver tongs for Cynthia when she was married. And, later on, a small, embossed, golden baby ring, to honor the birth of our first grandchild. After every possible attempt, we have never been able to explain their appearance in our home.

We have come to savor these happenings. They give a sense of the continuity of the past with the present and with the future. These elusive spirits seem gracious, thoughtful—only occasionally frightening—and thoroughly entertaining. Now we wonder: if the time comes for us to move again, is there any way we can take our other-worldly friends with us?

I Don't Believe in Ghosts, But...

by Jhan Robbins

I LIKE ghost stories. The eerier the better. But when the story is over and the hair on my head is lying flat again, I invariably laugh and say, "Of course no sensible person believes in ghosts."

Until recently. Now I don't know.

I was in London several years ago and decided to drive up to Oxford to do some research in one of the libraries there. On the evening of Wednesday the 18th, at the close of a bone-chilling, rainy day, I rented a motorcar and set out on Highway A40. Passing through West Wycombe, a village of brick and half-timbered houses so quaint that time seems to have bypassed it, I stopped at the George and Dragon Inn.

The menu was pure 18th-century English: mutton broth, steak and kidney pie, treacle pudding. When my pudding arrived, I noticed a large hole on one side—as though someone had put a thumb in it. I mentioned this to the waitress. "Oh, rot!" she exclaimed. "The White Lady's walking again. I do wish she'd keep out of the kitchen."

"The White Lady?" I inquired.

"Oh, she's our regular ghost," the waitress said.

Later, I asked John Boon, the ruddy-faced proprietor, whether he had a resident ghost.

"Yes, indeed," he replied. "And she's a bit troublesome at times. Sorry about the pudding. The fact is we don't quite know how to deal with her. She was a poor serving girl who was killed in one of the chalk caves down the road. There's an underground tunnel that leads from the inn to the caves. She was victimized. Very sad tale." He nodded toward the larger room beyond, quite clearly the village pub or "local." "Lift a few glasses in there and you'll get the whole story."

Among the occupants of the pub that night were a chairmaker who had a bristly, upturned mustache; a bricklayer who still wore his striped work apron; a young man in checked vest and black derby; a red-haired woman whose family had been five generations in West Wycombe. It was these four, largely, who recounted the story of "the White Lady of the local."

It happened 200 years ago. The White Lady, whom my narrators called Sukie, was 16 years old. She worked long hours at the George and Dragon. With two other girls she shared a bare little room in a chilly and distant wing of the inn.

Sukie was an extraordinarily pretty girl, with golden hair and a delicately turned figure. She was well-mannered; indeed, she gave herself such airs and graces that the other servants mockingly called her "your ladyship." She was ambitious to raise herself in life through a good marriage—and there were three likely prospects among the habitués of the inn. She set her cap for all three at once. So occupied did she become with the simultaneous flirtations that she took to dreamily tripping over doorsills, spilling soup on the customers, and confusing or forgetting her instructions.

One rainy night, a handsome young stranger rode up to the inn, left his muddied and exhausted stallion in the hands of the hostler, and sat wearily down at one of the copper-sheathed tables in the public room. A tankard of ale revived him, and he winked cheerily at pretty Sukie as she set his dinner in front of him.

Sukie became so confused that her thumb slipped into the bowl of treacle pudding, splashing a blob of it onto the young man's knee. She blushed and gasped, but the young man only laughed. The landlord, in a rage, boxed poor Sukie's ears and sent her weeping from the room.

The unknown rider returned the next night, and for a month he came several times a week, always looking for Sukie. He would pinch her pretty cheek and make her giggle with some foolish flattery. He had introduced himself to no one, but from the cut of his rich clothing and the conformation of his horse he was clearly either a prosperous highwayman or to the manor born. Sukie preferred to think the latter, and went around humming and dreaming—and more useless than ever.

Meanwhile, her other admirers scowled jealously from the far end of the dark-raftered room. As Sukie continued to ignore them, they concocted a crude practical joke to "bring her to her senses."

A scullery lad was sent to Sukie with a whispered message, purportedly from her mysterious lover. "'E said to tell you 'e's a noble lord and 'e wants to make you 'is lady," the lad said. "Meet 'im at the chalk caves at ten tomorrow night, and wear a proper wedding gown."

Poor Sukie swallowed the bait. She dashed up to her mistress's bedroom, ripped the linen sheets off the bed, and within the next 24 hours stitched up a handsome, full-skirted white dress. And at the appointed time she hurried along the damp tunnel to the chalk caves.

There, of course, she found only her three jilted sweethearts—a little drunk and roaring with laughter. "Here comes her ladyship!" they cried. "Welcome, my lady!"

Half mad with fury, she picked up lumps of soft chalk and hurled them at her tormentors. But then, as she whirled to run back, they caught her, pinched her and kissed her and spun her around. She kicked and clawed at them. In the scuffle she fell, striking her head on the wall. Frightened and remorseful, the men carried her, unconscious, back through the tunnel to the inn and to her bed. Then they tiptoed away.

In the morning, the other girls found Sukie dead. Her three suitors told what had happened. But the sheriff and the local curate looked at the body and felt that Sukie had not died of physical injury. Perhaps, they suggested, it was from humiliation and a broken heart.

Neither Sukie's aristocratic-looking lover nor his flashy chestnut steed was ever seen again. But a few days after Sukie's burial the two maids who shared her room moved out. Strange things were going on in that room, they declared, and they wanted no part of it.

THE TALE ended, I went into the kitchen and asked the proprietor if I might spend the night in Sukie's room.

"If you really want to," he said doubtfully. "We've got other rooms. My own dog won't go in there. If the White Lady had her thumb in the pudding tonight, she'll be there, mark you."

"What happens?" I asked.

He shrugged. "Depends. Some say they see a Lady all decked out in diamonds with a coronet on her head. Most say they just—well—see and feel something. It's uncomfortable, that's all I know. You haven't got high blood pressure or anything, have you?"

A little while later, I was tucked up in bed in the room where I was told that poor Sukie had met her end. I read a while, yawned, then pulled the chain on the room's only electric light—a single bulb fixed to the wall behind my head—and in a few minutes was asleep.

Many stories of ghostly encounters begin with "I don't know what woke me." I was sure I knew what woke me. Some joker had sneaked in and put a damp, cold hand on my forehead. Or an ice-cold slice of liver, more likely. Anything to panic the Yankee tourist. I angrily yanked the light chain. No one was in the room. There was nothing on my forehead.

The phenomenon was repeated several times. Cold hand. Snap on light. Cold hand goes away. Snap off light. Cold hand again. At length, I got the message. Something wanted me awake, but in the dark. I turned off the light and sat up, eyes open, staring into blackness.

Almost at once, I saw a pinpoint of light glowing about three feet off the ground near the door. A pencil flashlight aimed through the keyhole, I thought scornfully. I watched the shaft of light grow wider and stronger. It had an opaque, pearly quality. The apparition of the White Lady—if indeed it was she—was now about two feet in diameter and four feet high, still hovering near the doorway.

I turned on the electric bulb. The room looked as it had before—bare and ordinary. I turned it off again, and the strange light reappeared. I flung back the covers and, carrying my heavy book in one hand, walked resolutely toward the door. Any prankster lurking in the hallway was going to get a good clout.

A few feet from the door, I abruptly entered a zone of intense cold. My breath became labored. My arms and legs felt heavy. Was I having a heart attack? Was I just plain funking out from fear?

As I stood there, I was swept by a sudden, anguished depression—*Weltschmerz,* world sadness. Life seemed futile, beset by tragedy. "Life must have felt this way to poor Sukie," I thought, "with no one to stand up and protect her dignity."

At this sympathetic feeling, the light ballooned forward and seemed to reach for me. I backed hastily across the room, jumped into bed and yanked the electric light on.

I tried to think. The power of suggestion—was that why I was seeing a ghost? But if the ghost was only an emanation from my own subconscious, why wasn't it as I'd been told, a beautiful lady in white who wore diamonds—instead of a formless blob that looked more like a large, floating oyster and felt colder than sea water?

I considered the possibility of some kind of clairvoyance. A message from home, perhaps? I looked at my watch—3:15 a.m. My thoughts flashed across the sea to our Connecticut farmhouse, where my wife was alone with our younger son.

In this less than cheerful frame of mind, I waited for daylight. Breakfast, I had been told, was at seven. I was in the dining room, dressed and packed, five minutes early.

"Well, did you see anything of the White Lady?" the landlord inquired.

I told him what I had experienced. He nodded. "That's her, all right. Some claim she's looking for her lost lover. Others say she's out to find her murderers. My wife tells me I should have a priest in to lay her ghost to rest—there's a regular church ritual for that, you know. But I daresay she brings in some trade. Will you be stopping here on your return from Oxford?"

"Quite likely," I said bravely. But when I drove through West Wycombe a few days later on my way back, I was behind schedule and caught only a fleeting glimpse of its imposing roof lines as I sped on to London. I honked as I went past.

THIS story, like all proper ghost tales, has an epilogue. When I returned home the following week, my wife greeted me excitedly. "You know, I had the strangest experience one night," she said. "I went to bed early, and just as I was drifting off to sleep I heard you calling me. I jumped out of bed and thought I saw the lights of a taxi in the driveway. I was sure you were standing on the terrace, shouting to get in. I ran downstairs and opened the door. There was no one—nothing. But I tell you, I heard your voice! I saw a light! It was weird!"

"You must have heard a truck shifting gears," I said. "And you probably forgot to turn off the front light, as usual. Ah— by the way, when was this experience?"

She said promptly, "Last Wednesday at a quarter after ten."

Allowing for the five-hour time difference, this was exactly when I was dealing with the presence of the White Lady. You figure it out. I prefer not to try.

Believe It or Not

The Petrified Woman

by Loren C. Eiseley

IN THE proper books, you understand, there is no such thing as a petrified woman. I knew that, because I was a professional bone hunter. But bone hunters, like the men of other professions, have bad seasons. We had made queries in a score of western towns and tramped as many canyons. We had sent the institution for which we worked a total of one Oligocene turtle and a bag of rhinoceros bones. Our luck had to change. Somewhere there had to be fossils.

I was cogitating on the problem under a coating of lather in a barber shop with an 1890 chair when I became aware of a voice. You can hear a lot of odd conversation in barber shops, particularly in the back country. What caught my ear was something about "petrified." "I'm a-tellin' ya," the man's voice boomed. "A petrified woman, right out in that canyon. But he won't show it, not to nobody."

I managed to push an ear up through the lather. "Mister," I said, "I'm reckoned a kind of specialist in these matters. Where is this woman, and how do you know she's petrified?"

I knew perfectly well she wasn't, of course. Flesh doesn't petrify like wood or bone. Just the same, you can never tell what will turn up. Once I had a mammoth vertebra handed to me with the explanation that it was a petrified griddle cake.

Yes, he told me, the woman was petrified, all right. Old Man Buzby wasn't a feller to say it if 'tweren't so. And it weren't no part of a woman; it was a *whole* woman. Buzby

171

had said that, too. But Buzby was a queer one. An old bachelor, you know. And when the boys had wanted to see it, the old man had clammed up on where it was. A keepin' it all to his-self, he was. But seein' as I was interested in these things and a stranger, he might talk to me and no harm done. It was the trail to the right and out and up to the overhang of the hills. A little tar-papered shack there.

I asked Mack to go up with me. He was silent company, but one of the best bone hunters we had. In a day we reached the place. When I got out of the car, I knew the wind had been blowing there since time began. There was a rusty pump in the yard, and rusty wire and rusty machines nestled in the lee of a wind-carved butte. Everything was leaching and blowing away by degrees, even the tar paper on the roof. Out of the door came Buzby. There was an air of faded dignity about him.

Now in that country there is a sort of etiquette. You don't drive out to a man's place, a bachelor's, and you a stranger, and come up to his door and say, "I heard in town you got a petrified woman here and, brother, I sure would like to see it." You've got to use tact, same as anywhere else.

You get out of your jeep slowly, while the starved hounds look you over and get their barking done. You fumble for your pipe and explain casually you're doin' a little lookin' around in the hills. About then the person glimpses the equipment you're carrying and generally jumps to the conclusion that you're scouting for oil. You can see the hope flame up in his eyes and die down again as you explain that you're just hunting for bones.

But Buzby wasn't the type. I don't think he even thought of oil. He was small and neat and wore pince-nez glasses. I could see at a glance that he was a city man dropped, like a seed, by the wind. He had been there a long time.

At the back of the house we found the skull of a big, long-horned, extinct bison hung up under the eaves. It was a nice find, and we coveted it.

Buzby invited us into the neat two-room shack to see his collection of arrowheads. He was precise about his Indian relics as he was precise about everything. But I sensed, after a while, a touch of pathos—the pathos of a man clinging to order in a world where the wind changed the landscape before morning and not even a dog could help you contain the loneliness of your days.

"Someone told me in town you might have a wonderful

fossil up here," I finally ventured, poking in a box of arrow-heads and watching his shy, tense face.

"That would be Ned Burner," he said. "He talks too much."

"I'd like to see it," I said, carefully avoiding the word *woman*. "It might be of great value to science."

He flushed angrily. "I don't want any of 'em hereabouts to see it," he cried passionately. "They'll laugh, and they'll break it, and it'll be gone like—like everything." He stopped, his dark eyes widening with pain.

"We are scientists, Mr. Buzby," I urged gently. "We're not here to break anything. We don't have to tell anyone what we see."

He seemed a little mollified at this; then a doubt struck him. "But you'd want to take her away, put her in a museum."

I noticed the "her," but ignored it. "Mr. Buzby," I said, "we would very much like to see your discovery. It might be that a museum would help you save it from vandals. I'll leave it to you. If you say no, we won't touch it, and we won't talk about it in town, either."

I could see him hesitating. It was plain that he wanted to show us, but the prospect was half-frightening. As he talked on, I began to see what he wanted. He intended to show it to us in the hope we would confirm his belief that it was a petrified woman. At last he said, "Why don't you camp here tonight, Doctor? Maybe in the morning—"

I remembered the sound of the wind the next morning. In that country the wind never stopped. I think everyone there was a little mad because of it. It starts on the flats and goes down into those canyons and through them with weird noises, flaking and blasting at every loose stone or leaning pinnacle. It scrapes the sand away from pipy concretions till they stand out like strange, distorted sculptures. It leaves great stones teetering on wineglass stems. I began to suspect what we'd find.

Once he had given his consent and started, Buzby hurried on ahead, eager and panting. Up. Down. Up. Over boulders and splintered deadfalls of timber. Higher and higher into the back country. Toward the last he outran us, and I couldn't hear what he was saying. The wind whipped it away.

But there he stood, finally, at a niche under the canyon wall. He had his hat off, and for a moment was oblivious to us. He might almost have been praying. "This must be it," I said to Mack. "Watch yourself." Then we stepped forward.

It was a concretion, of course—an oddly shaped lump of mineral matter—just as I had figured after seeing the wind at work in those miles of canyon. It wasn't a bad job, at that. There were some bumps in the right places, and marks that might be the face, if your imagination was strong. Mine wasn't just then.

Buzby didn't wait for me to speak. He blurted with a terrible intensity that embarrassed me, "She—she's beautiful, isn't she?"

"It's remarkable," I said. "Quite remarkable." And then I just stood there not knowing what to do.

He seized on my words with such painful hope that Mack backed off and started looking for fossils in places where he knew perfectly well there weren't any.

I didn't catch it all; I couldn't possibly. The words came out in a long, aching torrent—the torrent dammed up for years in the heart of a man not meant for this place, nor for the wind at night by the windows, nor the empty bed, nor the neighbors 20 miles away. You're tough at first. He must have been to stick there. And then suddenly you're old. You're old and you're beaten, and there must be something to talk to and to love. And if you haven't got it, you'll make it in your head or out of a stone in a canyon wall.

He had found her, and he had a myth of how she came there, and now he came up and talked to her in the long after-noon heat while the dust devils danced in his failing corn. It was progressive. I saw the symptoms. In another year, she would be talking to him.

"It's true, isn't it, Doctor?" he asked me, looking up with that rapt face, after kneeling beside the niche. "You can see it's her. You can see it plain as day." For the life of me I couldn't see anything except a red scar writhing on the brain of a living man who must have loved somebody once, beyond words and reason.

"Now, Mr. Buzby," I started to say then, and Mack came up and looked at me. This, in general, is when you launch into a careful explanation of how concretions are made, so that the layman will not make the same mistake again. Mack just stood there looking at me in that stolid way of his. I couldn't go on with it.

But I saw where this was going to end. I saw it suddenly and too late. I opened my mouth while Mr. Buzby clasped his hands and tried to regain his composure. I opened my mouth, and I lied in a way to damn me forever in the halls of science. "Mr. Buzby," I said, "that—er—figure is astonishing. It is a remarkable case of preservation. We must have it for the museum."

The light in his face was beautiful. He believed me now. He believed himself. He came up to the niche again, and touched her lovingly.

"It's okay," I whispered to Mack. "We won't have to pack the thing out. He'll never give her up."

That's where I was a fool. He came up to me, his eyes troubled and unsure, but very patient.

"I think you're right, Doctor," he said. "It's selfish of me. She'll be safer with you. If she stays here, somebody will smash her. I'm not well." He sat down on a rock and wiped his forehead. "I'm sure I'm not well. I'm sure she'll be safer with you. Only I don't want her in a glass case where people can stare at her. If you can promise that, I—"

"I can promise that," I said, meeting Mack's eyes across Buzby's shoulder.

"And if I come there, I can see her?"

I knew I would never meet him again in this life.

"Yes," I said. "You can see her there." I waited, and then I said, "We'll get the picks and plaster ready. Now that bison skull at your house . . ."

It was two days later, in the truck, that Mack spoke to me. "Doc."

"Yeah."

"You know what the Old Man is going to say about shipping that concretion. It's heavy. Must be three hundred pounds with the plaster."

"Yes, I know."

Mack was pulling up slow along the abutment of a bridge. It was the canyon of the big Piney. He got out and went to the rear of the truck. "Doc, give me a hand with this, will you?"

I took one end, and we heaved together. It's a long drop into the big Piney. I didn't look, but I heard the thing break on the stones.

"I wish I hadn't done that," I said.

"It was only a concretion," Mack answered. "The old geezer won't know."

"I don't like it," I said. "Another week in that wind and I'd have believed in her myself—maybe I do anyhow. Let's get out of here. I tell you I don't like it. I don't like it at all."

"It's a hundred more to Valentine," Mack said.

He put the map away and slid over and gave me the wheel.

Eddie Robinson
and the Bolt of Lightning

by Emily and Per Ola d'Aulaire

PATCHES OF ICE glistened like quicksilver in the headlights as 53-year-old Eddie Robinson guided the 42,000-pound tractor-trailer rig down Interstate 95 near Providence, R.I. It was 4 a.m., February 12, 1971. On an overpass, a lone car ahead suddenly skidded broadside across the highway. Robinson cut the wheel to the right, hoping to squeeze between the sluing vehicle and the guardrail of the bridge. In the rear-view mirror, he saw his trailer start to swing out, the first stage of a dreaded jackknife.

The car recovered safely, but Robinson's cab slammed through the guardrail and came to rest in midair, dangling from the trailer pin over another highway 40 feet below. Robinson's head had whiplashed backward, punching a hole through the rear window. Drenched with blood from head gashes and soaked with diesel fuel from the dripping tanks, Robinson had only one thought—to get out fast. Opening the door, he clawed up the side of the wreck and hoisted himself to the overpass above.

At a nearby hospital, doctors stitched, X-rayed, poked, prodded, medicated—and pronounced him a very lucky fellow. Only superficial wounds. By 11 a.m., he was on a bus, heading back up I-95 to his home in Falmouth, Maine, a suburb of Portland.

That night, Robinson suddenly sat up in bed, gasping with pain. Doris, his wife of 32 years, rushed him to a local doctor early next morning. When Robinson told him he had been thoroughly examined the day before and pronounced fit, the doctor assumed his patient was only feeling his bruises. He prescribed more painkillers and sent him home to rest.

Several days later, a letter arrived from the hospital saying there was some confusion with Robinson's X rays. The doctors suspected a more serious injury and recommended that he be re-examined. The new tests revealed a concussion, fractured ribs, back sprain, and hematoma of the left hip. Robinson didn't complain—it was not in his nature. He rested and waited to get better so he could return to work.

But his health grew worse. His vision narrowed. Sometimes the world seemed to disappear before his very eyes and he thought he was blacking out. One day he stumbled into the house, visibly shaken, to announce to Doris, "I lost the whole house for a minute. I must be going blind."

Dr. Albert Moulton, Jr., a Portland ophthalmologist, found that Robinson's vision was failing rapidly and put it down to brain damage. He told Robinson that it was likely he would be permanently blind within a few months. Robinson took the news calmly. When he got home, he called the Hadley School for the Blind in Winnetka, Ill., and arranged to take Braille and touch-typing lessons at home. By December 1971, Robinson could perceive only the difference between light and dark. His bright blue eyes had become fixed, like a doll's eyes, staring blankly ahead.

Other problems began to crop up. He lost much of the use of his right arm, and to read Braille he had to shift to his left hand. All the while he felt a circle of pressure tighten around his head, like a steel band.

Then his hearing began to go. Soon he couldn't hear Doris even when she shouted. Hearing aids helped, but it wasn't the same. He felt trapped. He'd always been active before, often working a 70-hour week; now all was darkness and quiet.

The husky truck driver kept his spirits up by focusing on his gratitude for simply being alive. No matter how bad things were, he consoled himself, there were others, somewhere, less fortunate than he.

Soon he began attending the Lutheran church across the street from his house. He forgot about feeling trapped. He rediscovered the sense of tranquility that comes only from within.

Robinson hated to have Doris doing his jobs, so he learned to handle outside chores by feel and memory. He coiled a rope around an iron post in the middle of the lawn, tied the other end to his mower and, by going round and round as the rope unwound, was able to keep most of the grass cut. He fixed the leaky roof of his house by climbing a ladder and feeling where the shingles had crumbled.

Robinson had never had time for animals before. Now he began noticing them as he puttered quietly around the garage. Something about the blind man made the birds, chipmunks, skunks and raccoons lose their fear, for they began to approach him. Robinson clucked at them and they chattered back. He brought them food which they ate from his hand.

On a chill January afternoon almost a year after the accident, a poultry truck overturned on a nearby highway. A young Bantam hen escaped from the wreck and made her way to Robinson's yard. When he and Doris found the fowl the next morning, her feet were frozen. They carried her to the cellar to warm her up. When Robinson heard the new creature clucking, he would cluck back—*took-took*. This became her name.

Took-Took soon became Robinson's favorite. He built her a lean-to in the yard and fashioned an elaborate series of covered passageways into the garage where she could keep him company. Like Robinson, the chicken overcame a handicap. After her frozen toes had sloughed off, she learned to strut around on her stump-like feet as deftly as any fully toed bird.

In the winter of 1975, after shoveling the driveway, Robinson had dinner and went to bed. That night he woke up to what he calls "neon signs flashing across my chest." His symptoms indicated heart problems, and he was hospitalized for observation for close to a month. He returned home in pain; his chest and arms reacted to the slightest exertion. Even walking up the cellar steps necessitated a nitroglycerin tablet.

Yet Robinson refused to alter his daily routine—working in his garage shop, listening to his ham radio, walking into town with Doris. And, as he had every night since he lost his sight, he went into the yard and said a prayer of thanks. "I came to realize that we fail to appreciate the many wonderful things that happen around us each day. We live too fast. I slowed down to enjoy my life and was thankful."

What Eddie Robinson didn't know at the time was that he would soon have something to be truly thankful about. On June 4, 1980, at 3:30 p.m., he was tinkering in the garage when there came the roll of thunder, then sudden rain on the roof. Using his cane to guide himself around the exterior wall of the garage, he called for Took-Took. He knew he shouldn't be out in the storm, but he was worried about her. Near a poplar at the rear of the building, he stopped to listen for her answering clucks, then heard a loud snap, like a whip cracking. Lightning had hit the tree, and the charge spilled over into the ground where Robinson stood, knocking him flat.

About 20 minutes later, when Robinson regained consciousness, he stumbled to a neighbor's house and asked for a drink of water. "I think I've been hit by lightning," he said, in a daze. With knees like rubber, he returned home, drank several more glasses of water, then went to bed.

An hour later, Robinson emerged from the bedroom, still unquenchably thirsty. He told Doris what had happened, downed a half-gallon of milk and slumped onto the sofa. Suddenly, he realized that he was seeing the wall plaque given to him by his grandchildren. "God couldn't be everywhere," he read haltingly, "so he made grandfathers."

"What did you say?" Doris called from the kitchen. Robinson let out a yell: "I can see that sign!" Disbelieving, Doris rushed to the living room. "What time is it?" she asked, pointing to the wall clock. "Five o'clock," he answered. "Doris, *I can see!*"

Doris noticed something else. "Where are your hearing aids?" she nearly screamed in her excitement. Robinson reached for his ears, but the devices were gone. "Dear God," said Robinson, "I can hear, too!"

The 62-year-old man felt immensely tired. He ached everywhere. Worried that the lightning might have done him harm, Doris phoned a doctor's answering service. She was told to contact the emergency medical team, if needed, during the night, and to come in to the doctor's office in the morning. All that night Doris sat up to monitor her husband's breathing, still not believing what had happened.

The next day the doctor pronounced him fine. And when Dr. Moulton examined his eyes, he verified the impossible. "I can't explain it," he said. "All I know is that he definitely could not see, and now he can."

In church that Sunday, Eddie asked the minister if he could speak briefly to the congregation. Since the accident, when it was time to go to the altar, he had been led by his wife or a friend. Not this time. When the minister motioned to him, Eddie danced up the aisle—an Irish jig, he claims—to say aloud a prayer that ended, "And I have three more words to add, Lord: Thank you. Amen."

Meanwhile, the wire services picked up the story and, almost overnight, Robinson was a celebrity. Newspapers called for interviews, photographers drove to Falmouth for a picture of Robinson and his pet chicken, TV cameras arrived. ABC Television arranged for Robinson to see his grandchildren, eight-year-old Christina and nine-year-old Kimberly, for the first time on its show, "Good Morning America."

While in New York for the show, Robinson suddenly realized he no longer had to stare straight ahead. His eyes had "unlocked." Later, staying with his son and grandchildren in Virginia, he noticed that feeling was creeping back into his right arm. In fact he felt so good he mowed his son's grass. "I didn't feel a twinge of angina pain," he recalls, "and haven't had to take a pill for my heart since the lightning."

The hateful "band" around his head disappeared. And some varicose veins in his right leg have improved.

DOCTORS who have examined Robinson are unable to explain why his physical problems should have abated just after the lightning struck. Were his blindness and deafness indeed caused by brain damage? Or was this a psychological reaction brought on by the trauma of the trucking accident? And did that bolt from the blue set everything right again, from top to bottom? Though some may argue and puzzle over the recovery, Eddie and his family don't. "It is an act of God," says Robinson simply. "What else could it be?"

In addition to his TV appearances, Robinson has spoken to schoolchildren, telling them what it is like to be blind—as someone who has been there and back. "I've seen more in the last three months than I had in a lifetime," he says. "I now appreciate the everyday wonders of life: moonlight filtering through the leaves, the flowers in the garden, a caterpillar spinning its cocoon.

"What's more, I never gave up hope. And maybe what happened to me will give others courage to never give up."

Meanwhile, his feelings about the whole ordeal are perhaps best summed up in a bumper sticker on his car: THANK GOD FOR MIRACLES.

Mary's Dream House

by Alexander Woollcott

I GIVE YOU this matter-of-fact short story as it first came to me—as something that befell a young woman from Catonsville, Md., while on her honeymoon in France, her first trip abroad. For convenience, let me call her Mary.

As she and her husband were motoring from Beaune to Bourges, this thing happened. On the edge of a small village they passed a modest estate—a shabby house of cream-colored plaster, standing some distance back from the highway. Midway was an oval fountain in which goldfish disported themselves. Mary caught at her husband's arm and asked him to stop and let her out. He watched while she ran to the high iron fence and stood peering between the palings, studying the large gate and the drive which led up past the garden. When she came back she was visibly shaken. "My dear," she said, "it's my house. The same in every particular."

She didn't have to explain. For years the family had been teasing Mary about her house. In her dreams she'd find herself in the same place—a house she'd never seen in a land she didn't know. She'd never once supposed there was such a place. She'd thought of it purely as a creation of her own subconscious. And now, driving along a road in France, she had come upon it and was seeing it with her open eyes.

After the first shock, Mary was delighted. She was all for exploring the place at once. Why, it might even be possible to rent it for a week or two—to bring her husband to her dream house and actually spend her honeymoon there!

As they approached the gate, a young priest was coming out. In her Catonsville French, Mary started to ask if the family were at home. The priest stared at her incredulously, then crossed himself and hurried down the road in the direction of the village.

Her husband, skeptical about the whole adventure, was delighted with the effect on the holy man of his bride's Maryland French. In hilarious moods they pushed open the gate and walked toward a gardener who was pruning the shrubbery. *"M'sieu, est-ce que vous pouvez me dire . . . ?"* But she got no further. Straightening up to answer her, the gardener took one look, dropped his shears and ran as if the devil were after him.

This was discouraging. But they pushed on to the house. At closer range a hundred details convinced her. It *was* her house. That row of oriel windows under the eaves, the Latin inscription over the door. The same. She was shaking with excitement as her husband gave a pull on the doorbell. They could hear the faint jangle in the distance. Then footsteps and the rattle of a bolt. The door was opened by an elderly woman in cap and apron. Before they could get three words out, she bent forward, stared at Mary as at some monster and slammed the door. They heard the bolt clang back into place.

With a mixture of irritation and bewilderment our friends went back to their car, relieved to find that it hadn't turned into smoke and drifted off over the treetops. "My dear," said the bridegroom, "they don't seem to like us."

At the village they found a promising inn. The innkeeper was an affable soul and they soon were pumping him about the house on the edge of town. Whose was it? Who lived in it? How old was it? Was it possible to rent it?

On the latter score he was doubtful. They mustn't quote him, but it was common talk in the village that the house was haunted. Off and on for the past ten years, the family, the workers on the place and even visitors, like M. le Curé, had seen a silent spirit roaming there. Funny that they should be asking about it at that moment, because he'd just heard that the place was in a turmoil. The ghost was walking again—in broad daylight and no longer silent. His own cook's son was the gardener there and even now was down in the kitchen drinking his head off and shaking like a leaf. He'd seen the ghost. Only an hour before, while he was pruning the syringas by the drive, it had appeared and spoken to him—the ghost of a young woman, accompanied this time, he said, by the ghost of a young man.

Well, there's the story. A number of years ago it appeared as a work of fiction, but before that I had already heard it by word of mouth. I think it likely that it really happened some-time . . . to somebody . . . somewhere.

Bewitching
Bamboozles

Three UFOs—
How Real Were They?

by Ronald Schiller

IN 1969, THE U.S. AIR FORCE ended a 22-year investigation of unidentified flying objects (UFOs). Its 8400-page report exposed some of the 12,618 sightings on record as hoaxes or hallucinations. But 95 percent proved to be simple misidentification of an incredible variety of normal phenomena: meteors, ball lightning, reflections of searchlights on clouds, weather balloons, rockets, even fireflies. Planes have attempted to intercept mirages, lens-shaped clouds, the planet Venus, and radar blips caused by temperature inversions.

UFOs in photographs have been identified as thrown Frisbees, superimpositions, models hanging from strings, dirt in the camera lens and processing blurs. Particularly deceptive are parhelia, or "sun dogs," bright circles caused by the sun's reflection on particles of ice in the atmosphere. Some may have a metallic appearance and an amber glow resembling a jet exhaust.

The government-funded report released in 1969 seemed to end the flying-saucer controversy for a time. But in 1973 thousands more sightings were reported. A Gallup poll revealed that 54 percent of Americans believed UFOs were real; 11 percent thought they might have seen one. A few scientists also entered the fold, notably J. Allen Hynek, then head of the astronomy department of Northwestern University, hailed by many as "the Galileo of Ufology," and James A. Harder, professor of civil engineering at the University of California in Berkeley.

When I asked Hynek, Harder and ten other leading Ufologists to recommend convincing encounters I might study, I was told that no "perfect" case exists. Nevertheless, the following three incidents were cited as among the best-authenticated cases on record.

On the night of October 18, 1973, while flying in clear weather at an altitude of 2500 feet near Mansfield, Ohio, the four-man crew of a U.S. Army helicopter were frightened by a glowing red object that seemed to be converging on them at immense speed. To avoid collision, the pilot, Capt. Lawrence Coyne, went into a quick descent. When he last observed the altimeter, it registered 1700 feet. With the glowing object still headed for the copter, he warned his crew to "brace for impact."

Instead, as Coyne later reported, "we looked up, and there was the object—stopped—about 500 feet above us." It appeared to be a gray metallic structure, 50 to 60 feet long, trailing a green light that flooded the cockpit. After a few seconds it took off at high speed, without turbulence, vortex or engine noise. When he next looked at his altimeter, Coyne was shocked to discover the helicopter was at 3500 feet and climbing, though he could not remember touching the controls. Had it been sucked up or drawn up magnetically by the UFO?

Another mystery: the radio, which functioned perfectly before and after, seemingly blacked out during the encounter, making it impossible to communicate with either the Akron or Mansfield airports. After landing at Cleveland, the crew learned that no other aircraft had been in the area of the encounter at the time.

Outside on his parents' farm the evening of November 2, 1971, Ronald Johnson, 16, of Delphos, Kan., heard a rumbling sound. Looking up, he saw a brightly illuminated, mushroom-shaped object hovering two feet above the ground in a grove of elm trees nearby. As the boy watched, the glow from the propulsion unit beneath the object became more intense, the rumble changed to a high-pitched whine, and the vehicle ascended and took off at considerable speed.

Ronald lost his vision for about ten minutes. On recovering, he called his parents out in time to see a bright light receding in the sky. Examining the area where the object had been, the Johnsons saw a glowing, grayish-white ring, eight feet in diameter. Nearby trees were also aglow. When the Johnsons touched the luminescent soil, their fingertips turned numb. (The numbness in Mrs. Johnson's case lasted for weeks.) Mrs. Johnson took Polaroid pictures of the area.

The ring, presumably baked into the soil by the heat of the UFO's engine, soon lost its glow. But the ring persisted for months, apparently impervious to rain and growing things, except for mushrooms. Its whitish soil was 14 inches deep.

At 6:15 p.m. on November 5, 1975, near Heber, Ariz., seven young woodcutters, returning home by truck, spotted a large, hovering object that looked like a flying saucer. Travis Walton, 22, jumped from the truck and ran toward it, whereupon he was zapped to the ground by an intense glowing beam from the craft. His companions drove off in panic. They returned a short time later, but Walton had disappeared and could not be found even after days of intensive search.

On November 11, the missing man called relatives from a telephone booth on the outskirts of Heber. He was reportedly in a confused mental state, babbling a story of having been abducted aboard the UFO and subjected to close examination. Later, under hypnosis, he described his captors as looking like "well-developed fetuses" about five feet tall, with hairless, domed heads and large brown eyes.

The six young men who witnessed the event were given lie-detector tests. Five passed; results for the sixth were indecisive. Three months later Walton himself took a lie-detector test and passed it.

To many of the Ufologists who investigated them, these three cases seemed unassailable. "The evidence," stated Harder, "is as valid as any that would be accepted in an American criminal court. It is beyond any reasonable doubt." And so it might have remained but for Philip Klass, an editor of *Aviation Week & Space Technology*, an indefatigable investigator whose avocation is debunking the supernatural. This is what he argues:

Case 1. The glowing object witnessed by the helicopter crew in Ohio, Klass quickly became convinced, was probably a "fireball," one of the shower of Orionid meteors whose peak activity occurs precisely at that time of the year and hour of the night. He doubted it was converging on the helicopter; the distance of meteors is notoriously difficult to judge. (In 1969, the pilots of an American Airlines plane thought they were on a near-collision course with meteors that actually passed *.125 miles* north of them.) The "gray metallic structure" was probably also an illusion. People in Indiana and Tennessee who watched flaming pieces of a Soviet Zond-4 rocket booster re-enter the atmosphere, on a night in 1968, noted Klass, also reported seeing nonexistent "cigar-shaped metallic objects with lighted windows."

What the helicopter crew actually saw hovering overhead, Klass believed, was the after-image of the meteor and its luminous tail, imprinted on their retinas. That the helicopter cockpit was suffused with green light is not surprising: its plastic canopy was tinted green. The reason the crew could not reach Akron by radio was because, at their reduced altitude, they were out of range. Failure to raise the nearby Mansfield tower may have been due to the haste with which the panicky operator was switching frequencies.

As for being "sucked up" by some mysterious force: given their altitude and rate of descent, the helicopter was due to hit the ground in less than 30 seconds. Klass surmised that the experienced pilot sensed the danger and pulled up instinctively even though he did not remember doing so.

Coyne and Ufologists remained unconvinced by the meteor theory, however. They pointed out that a fireball lasts only a few seconds, and it does not "appear to stop" as Coyne and his crew reported happened in this case.

Case 2. The purported UFO landing on the farm in Kansas rests on the unsupported testimony (no lie-detector tests) of Ronald Johnson and his parents, and the mysterious white ring on the ground allegedly created by UFO exhaust gases. But if the gases were hot enough to bake the earth 14 inches deep, they should have incinerated every twig and tree in the area. Yet the next day, the sheriff and his deputies found "no evidence of burning of any kind."

Klass's photographic expert, shown pictures taken by Mrs. Johnson the night of the landing, identified the "luminescence" emanating from the ring in one as the reflected illumination of a flash bulb, and the glow on nearby tree trunks in another as a reflection of the setting sun. (It appeared on the sides of the trunks facing away from the UFO ring.) Klass suspected the circle was a "fairy ring," one of those natural circular formations that appear on lawns and golf courses in which little will grow except fungus. Samples of the soil examined 24 hours after the incident revealed it was neither luminescent nor radioactive.

The behavior of the Johnson family also seemed curious to Klass. They later claimed that UFOs had returned to the farm several times, and that a "wolf girl" had appeared in the vicinity. Strangest of all was Ronald Johnson's assertion that still-immature lambs, born shortly before and after the UFO visit, gave birth—without benefit of impregnation by rams— to tiny lambs of their own. These all died and he disposed of their carcasses without showing them to anyone.

Case 3. The seemingly incontrovertible evidence of the multiple polygraph tests in the Travis Walton abduction case also turned sour under probing by Klass. The tests which five of the young woodcutters passed had been arranged by law officials to determine if they had killed or injured their missing friend—with a final question, an afterthought, asking whether they had actually seen a UFO. "That one question does not make it a valid test so far as verifying the UFO incident," stated polygraph operator C. E. Gilson.

More startling was the discovery that Walton himself had taken a three-hour polygraph test four days after his reappearance—*and flunked it.* The experienced examiner, John J. McCarthy, concluded the subject "was attempting to perpetrate a UFO hoax." The results were not revealed because McCarthy had been pledged to secrecy by APRO (the Aerial Phenomena Research Organization), and by the *National Enquirer,* which paid for the examination. Both organizations omitted mention of the failed test in their publications.

The test that Travis Walton did manage to pass three months later, at the behest of APRO, was administered by an operator who agreed to confine himself to questions *written out for him in advance*—a practically unheard-of procedure. "From my reading of the charts," stated Tom Ezell, the more experienced head of the Phoenix testing firm, "you would not be able to say if Walton is telling the truth or lying."

When questioned under hypnosis at a session attended by psychiatrist Dr. Jean Rosenbaum, Walton admitted to being a "UFO freak." In fact, just prior to the incident, he had told his mother that if he was ever abducted by a UFO she was not to worry because "I'll be all right."

Rosenbaum concluded that Travis had been hallucinating at the time of the incident. "He is telling the truth when he says it happened, but it is his own truth. On the level of objective reality, it did not happen." After an independent examination of the subject, another psychiatrist reached the same conclusions.

All these disclosures have failed to convince many Ufologists. The three incidents are still cited as "classic encounters" in the UFO literature.

And so the surrealistic debate goes on. Are these alien spaceships, or figments of the imagination? The one inescapable fact that emerges is that, despite the millions of UFO landings that have supposedly taken place on earth, not a single piece of tangible evidence—neither a nut, bolt, artifact, instrument or defector from a flying saucer, nor even a convincing picture of one—has ever been produced.

What's the Truth
About the Bermuda Triangle?

by James Stewart-Gordon

AT 2:10 p.m. on December 5, 1945, five U.S. Navy training planes took off in clear weather from Fort Lauderdale, Fla., flew east over coastal waters—and disappeared into seemingly insoluble mystery. This was Flight 19, Lt. C. C. Taylor commanding four student pilots and their crews—14 men in all. Flight 19's mission was a navigational training run between Florida and the Bahamas.

At about 3:40, Taylor reported that his compasses—both gyro and magnetic—were not reading properly. Flight 19 followed its leader aimlessly, first east, then west, then northeast over the ocean, as he tried to get his bearings by radio. Then, suddenly, Taylor was heard to give orders to ditch. And, not long after, all contact was lost.

Quickly, two Martin Mariners—giant seaplanes designed for long-range patrols—were dispatched to search for Flight 19. Several hours later, the wind kicked up to 30 knots and visibility became limited. A return to base was ordered. Only one Mariner landed. For days thereafter, the Navy and Coast Guard combed a 100,000-square-mile area with more than 100 planes and surface craft, but no trace was ever found of Flight 19 or the other Mariner.

Today, over 35 years after the tragedy, Flight 19 and the lost Martin Mariner are still central characters in a mystery that has set spines atingle the world over. Journalists, authors, television producers and psychics have noted the disappearance of many another ship and plane in the southwestern quadrant of the North Atlantic—and have created there a haunting zone called the Bermuda Triangle, where ships are found deserted with warm food in their galleys, planes vanish immediately after signaling that they are landing, and navigational compasses behave as if bewitched.

Apexes of the Triangle are Bermuda, Puerto Rico and a point in the Gulf of Mexico west of Florida. It is a watery Jekyll-and-Hyde world of tiny coral islands, glittery beaches and blissfully beautiful waters, where itinerant hazes, powerful currents and sudden storms lurk behind a deceptively smiling exterior. One can never know, it appears, when that smile may turn into a snarl.

While controversy mounts over whether the Triangle's deadly influences—which, as the story goes, have accounted for 35 ships and planes since 1946—can be explained by science or must be attributed to supernatural forces, fascination with the subject has produced a torrent of books, films, TV specials. At the very top of best-seller lists has appeared *The Bermuda Triangle*, by linguist and scuba diver Charles Berlitz. Two paperbacks, *The Devil's Triangle* by Richard Winer, and *Limbo of the Lost* by John Wallace Spencer, have sold nearly three million copies in the past two years.

Of the alleged 40 ships and 20 planes lost mysteriously during the last 100 years, 21 have met misfortune in the months of December and January, when boreal blasts and the Christmas Winds blow across the Triangle, bringing huge swells. Three of the most celebrated victims—including Flight 19—have appeared or disappeared on the same date: December 5.

The first, the brig *Mary Celeste,* was discovered rocking gently on a calm, misty morning in 1872 near the Azores (to whose boundaries the influence of the Triangle is presumed by some to reach). Sails set and cargo intact, she had been deserted by her captain and eight-man crew. The mystery remains unsolved. Exactly 74 years later, and a year after the loss of Flight 19, the Bahamas schooner *City Belle* was found south of the Bahamas, deserted by her crew. Her fate has never been explained.

The largest ship the Triangle has claimed is the U.S.S. *Cyclops,* a 19,000-ton Navy collier bound from Rio de Janeiro

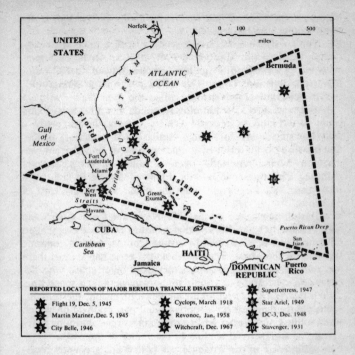

REPORTED LOCATIONS OF MAJOR BERMUDA TRIANGLE DISASTERS:

1	Flight 19, Dec. 5, 1945	**4**	Cyclops, March 1918	**7**	Superfortress, 1947
2	Martin Mariner, Dec. 5, 1945	**5**	Revonoc, Jan. 1958	**8**	Star Ariel, 1949
3	City Belle, 1946	**6**	Witchcraft, Dec. 1967	**9**	DC-3, Dec. 1948
				10	Stavenger, 1931

to Norfolk with a cargo of manganese ore. She disappeared in March 1918, carrying a 293-man crew and a mysteriously silent wireless with her.

The Triangle is also credited with swallowing up the yacht *Revonoc* in January 1958 with her owner (millionaire publisher Harvey Conover) and four-man crew while they were cruising from Key West to Miami. Only traces of the *Revonoc:* a smashed lifeboat and a toilet seat.

Equally puzzling is the case of the 23-foot cabin cruiser *Witchcraft,* which set out from Miami on the night of December 22, 1967, when her owner and a passenger decided to view the city's Christmas lights. A few hours later, the owner radioed Miami Coast Guard that *Witchcraft* needed assistance—she had damaged her propeller and was adrift near the harbor channel entrance, from which they could see Miami. Within ten minutes, the Coast Guard was on the spot—but no sign of the cruiser has ever been found.

The air above the Triangle seems just as conducive to vanishing acts. In the summer of 1947, a U.S. Air Force Superfortress reporting no difficulties was swallowed up 100 miles from the Bermuda coast. The following year, on January 30, a British commercial airliner called the *Star Tiger*, with 31 aboard, vanished after radioing Bermuda that all was well and they would land on schedule. (One year later, the *Star Ariel*—a sister ship—was lost under similar circumstances.) In December 1948, the pilot of a chartered DC-3 bound from San Juan to Miami reported—over the sound of his passengers singing Christmas carols—the lights of Miami in sight. All was calm, all was bright—but the plane was never heard of again.

Despite insistence by the U.S. Navy, the Coast Guard and the National Ocean Survey that disasters within the so-called Triangle can be explained by natural causes, cultists continue to suspect the worst. They attribute the eerie happenings there to such diabolic forces as: visitors from outer space who descend in spaceships to gobble up human victims; a space-time warp that traps its victims in another dimension; the remains of a giant prism left by a sophisticated past civilization which sends out sinister rays when lunar and astral conditions reactivate it; a giant void leading to the center of the earth.

As interest in the Triangle has boiled up, a counter-revolution has set in. Larry Kusche, a technical writer in Phoenix, Arizona, wrote a book, *The Bermuda Triangle Mystery—Solved*, which exposes Triangle fables case by case. The fabulists, according to Kusche, instead of looking for logical solutions, have copied each other's mistakes, embroidering details until what really happened has been obscured by the elaborate crewel work of pure romance.

For example, someone once recorded that in 1931 a ship of Norwegian registry called the *Stavenger* had vanished in the Triangle with all hands. Ever since, the *Stavenger* has usually been on Triangle cultists' lists. Kusche, by checking the records, discovered that there was no *Stavenger* under Norwegian flag in 1931. As for the *City Belle*, battered by a sudden storm, she had signaled that she was in distress. Her signal was picked up by the American base on Great Exuma, and her crew was rescued. Bang goes another legend!

Launching into the tale of the *Cyclops,* Kusche reported that a diver working on another job near Norfolk, Va., in 1968 spotted what could have been her wreckage, resting on the bottom. The cause of her demise, as advanced by the Coast Guard, is that she may have been hit broadside by a sudden wave, caving in her hatch covers. Then seas filled her hold, waterlogging her top-heavy cargo and tipping her over before anyone could send out an SOS.

Add to all the other hazards the fact that the Straits of Florida are among the busiest waterways in the world. In the haze common here, large ships sometimes run down smaller craft with no more than a slight, unnoticed bump. From the bits of wreckage located, the Coast Guard thinks that is what could have happened to the unhappy yacht *Revonoc.*

Capt. Adrian Lonsdale, of the Coast Guard, is convinced that meteorological disturbances, mechanical failure and human error are the causes of the disasters. He adds, "The loss of the *Witchcraft* is a perfect example of all three. The night was windy, and one propeller was damaged, which reduced her speed. She had a Bermuda top—a canvas covering which acted like a sail. Between the action of the currents, the effect of the wind on her top, and her reduced speed, she was probably carried north toward Ft. Lauderdale. From the sea, Lauderdale looks like Miami. When *Witchcraft* radioed that she was off Miami, she was actually off Lauderdale. We were looking in the wrong place. She must eventually have been carried out to sea, and that was the end of that."

Even the most experienced aircraft pilots can encounter trouble in such an unpredictable area. In 1962, Coast Guard Capt. Marshall Phillips, flying a routine sweep, found himself without warning in the grip of a thunderstorm. In seconds, his plane was thrust violently downward, then upward like a slingshot pellet, as the cloud's unleashed forces clawed at his plane's wings, almost snapping them off. Phillips got clear, only to discover himself flying upside down at 8000 feet. He did not panic—and managed to right his plane and return to base. In his opinion, the Superfortress that vanished in 1947 must have flown into just such a thunderstorm—invisible to radar—and been destroyed.

Commenting on the lost DC-3 and its carolers, Phillips says, "Before takeoff the pilot reported that the batteries in his radio-sending equipment were weak. Then the wind had shifted strongly and, instead of being over south Florida, he was probably over the Gulf of Mexico and mistaking the lights of Key West for Miami. Finally, he ran out of gas and crashed." In the Coast Guard's opinion, the two British *Star* planes could have run into thunderstorms, causing them to disintegrate, or—more likely—driving them off course beyond the range of their radio equipment. They went down when their fuel was exhausted.

Flight 19 was lost not because of supernatural forces but because Taylor lost his bearings. He failed to switch to his clear emergency radio channel, which would have made it more likely for shore stations to give him a fix on his position; and finally panic seems to have moved in.

As for the lost Martin Mariner, the freighter *Gaines Mills* reported a tremendous fiery bang at 7:50 p.m. in the area where the plane was flying. The known susceptibility of Martin Mariners to develop loose fuel connections in the face of turbulence and then to blow up supplies its own answer.

Captain Lonsdale sums up: "Lloyd's of London reports an average of 352 major ships a year (exclusive of pleasure craft and light planes) lost throughout the world. Four or five of these are stricken so suddenly that they have no time to send out an SOS. If a ship is lost in a violent storm in what is known as the Triangle, to us it's a disaster. To someone who doesn't know the facts, it's uncanny. I guess anything you can't understand yourself is bound to be supernatural."

Astral Projection and the Horse That Could Count

by Carl Sagan

IN THE SECOND CENTURY A.D., there lived in Greece a handsome, clever and totally unscrupulous con man, Alexander of Abonutichus. In his most famous imposture, he rushed into the crowded marketplace and predicted the advent of a new god. He then raced to the construction site of a new temple, the crowd streaming after him, and "discovered"—where he had previously emplaced it—a goose egg in which he had sealed a baby snake. Opening the egg, he announced the snakelet as the god he had prophesied.

After retiring to his house for a few days, Alexander admitted the breathless multitudes, who observed his body now entwined with a large serpent. The serpent was, in fact, a conveniently docile variety outfitted with a linen head of somewhat human countenance. The room was dimly lit. Because of the press of the crowd, no visitor could stay for long or inspect the serpent carefully. The opinion was that Alexander had, indeed, delivered a god.

Alexander then announced that the god would answer any written questions that were delivered to him in sealed envelopes. When alone, he would read the message, reseal the envelope and attach an oracular answer. People flocked to this marvel. The result: an income for Alexander equivalent to several hundred thousand dollars per year and fame rivaled by few men of his time.

We may smile at Alexander the Oracle-Monger. We would not nowadays be taken in by such a fraud. Or would we? In Alexander's time, efforts to bamboozle the public often involved religion. This is, of course, still being done. But in the past 100 years, science has emerged as the primary means of penetrating the secrets of the universe, and so we should expect many contemporary deceptions to have a scientific ring. And they do.

Today claims are made at the edge of science—assertions that excite popular interest and, in many cases, that would be of profound scientific importance if they were true. They are out of the ordinary, a break from the humdrum, and often imply that we have vast, untapped powers, for instance; or that unseen forces are about to save us from ourselves, or destroy us.

Well, science does sometimes make such claims: that the hereditary information passed from generation to generation is encoded in a single molecule called DNA; in the discovery of continental drift; in the tapping of nuclear energy. So if some additional claim is made—for example, that it is possible to float unaided in the air, by effort of will alone—what is so different about that? Nothing. Except for the matter of proof. Many claims of levitation have been made in the past 100 years, but photographs of people rising 15 feet into the air have never been taken under conditions that exclude possible fraud.

Take another example, something called astral projection. Under conditions of religious ecstasy or hypnagogic sleep or sometimes under the influence of a hallucinogen, people report the distinct sensation of stepping outside the body and effortlessly floating to some other place. But the fact that a sensation is reported does not mean that it occurred as claimed. Perhaps there is a common wiring defect in human neuroanatomy that under certain circumstances always leads to the same illusion of astral projection. To my knowledge, no demonstration of astral projection has ever been reported under controlled circumstances with skeptics in attendance.

While some claims at the edge of science may be the product of outright fraud, most appear to be due to a lack of vigorous skepticism on the part of the believers. In the early 1900s, there was a horse in Germany that could read and do mathematics. Or so it seemed. The horse, named Clever Hans, was owned by Wilhelm von Osten, whose character was such, everyone said, that fraud was out of the question. Distinguished scientists viewed the equine marvel and pronounced it genuine. Hans would reply to questions put to him by coded taps (one for yes, say, and two for no). Someone would ask, "Hans, how much is twice the square root of nine, less one?" After a pause, Hans would raise his right foreleg and tap five times. Was Moscow the capital of Russia? Two taps. How about St. Petersburg? One tap.

The Prussian Academy of Sciences sent a commission, headed by Oskar Pfungst, to investigate. Pfungst noticed that the more difficult the question, the longer it took Hans to answer. When Von Osten did not know the answer, Hans exhibited a comparable ignorance. When the horse was blindfolded, no answers were forthcoming. The phenomenon then seemed clear. When a question was put to Hans, Von Osten would become slightly tense, for fear that the horse would make the wrong number of taps. When Hans reached the correct number, Von Osten unconsciously and imperceptibly relaxed—imperceptibly to virtually all human observers but not to Hans, who was rewarded with a sugar cube for correct answers. Hans was totally ignorant of mathematics but very sensitive to nonverbal cues.

Perhaps the most popular claims of pseudoscience have to do with the Bermuda Triangle, flying saucers and ancient astronauts. Advocates of ancient astronauts assert that numerous pieces of archeological evidence can be understood only in terms of our ancestors having had contact with extraterrestrial-civilizations. An iron pillar in India; the pyramids of Egypt; the stone monoliths on Easter Island; and the geometrical figures in Nazca, Peru, are each alleged to have been manufactured by or under the supervision of extraterrestrials. But these artifacts have plausible and much simpler explanations, all based on human intelligence and hard work.

The interest in UFOs and ancient astronauts seems at least partly due to unfulfilled religious needs. The extraterrestrials are often described as wise, powerful, benign, and sometimes attired in long white robes. They are very much like gods and angels, coming from other planets rather than from heaven, using spaceships rather than wings. Indeed, one British survey suggests that more people believe in extraterrestrial visitations than in God.

Public interest in such matters as UFOs and ancient astronauts is, I believe, at least in part, a good thing. But our openness to the dazzling possibilities presented by modern science must be tempered by some hard-nosed skepticism. Many interesting possibilities simply turn out to be wrong. An openness to new possibilities and a willingness to ask hard questions are both required to advance our knowledge.

The extraordinary should certainly be pursued; but extraordinary claims require extraordinary evidence—the burden of proof should fall squarely on those who make the proposals. In the meantime, the best antidote for pseudoscience lies, I believe, in the documented wonders of science itself:

• There is an African freshwater fish that is nearly blind. It generates an electric field that enables it to distinguish between predators and prey and communicate in a fairly elaborate electrical language with other fish of the same species. This involves an organ system and sensory capability unknown to pretechnological human beings.

• Pigeons are now found to have a remarkable sensitivity to magnetism, evidently using this sensory capability for navigation and to sense their surroundings—a sensory modality never glimpsed by any human.

• Quasars seem to be violent galactic explosions that destroy millions of worlds, many of them perhaps inhabited.

• Each of our cells contains dozens of mitochondria, tiny factories that combine our food with molecular oxygen in order to extract energy in convenient form. Recent evidence suggests that billions of years ago, the mitochondria were free-living organisms that have slowly evolved into a mutually dependent relation with the cell. In a very real sense, then, we are not a single organism but an array of about ten trillion beings.

Such a list could be continued almost indefinitely. I believe that this smattering of findings in modern science is far more compelling and exciting than most of the doctrines of pseudoscience. Science is more intricate and subtle, reveals a much richer universe and powerfully evokes our sense of wonder. And it has the additional and important virtue of being true.

Frightening Fiction

The Most Dangerous Game

by Richard Connell

"OFF THERE TO THE RIGHT somewhere is what the old charts call Ship-Trap Island," said Whitney. "Sailors have a curious dread of the place. Some superstition . . ."

"Can't see it," remarked Rainsford, trying to peer through the dank tropical night that pressed in upon the yacht.

"It will be light enough when we reach Brazil in a few days," promised Whitney. "We should have some good hunting up the Amazon. Great sport, hunting."

"The best sport in the world," agreed Rainsford.

Later, his partner having gone below for the night, Rainsford stayed on deck to smoke another pipe. As he puffed, an abrupt sound startled him. Again, and again. Off in the blackness someone had fired a gun three times.

He strained his eyes in the direction, but it was like trying to see through a blanket. Rainsford leaped up on the rail to get greater elevation; his pipe, striking a rope, was knocked from his mouth. He lunged for it, lost his balance and fell into the blood-warm waters of the Caribbean. He struggled to the surface and shouted. Desperately he struck out after the receding lights of the yacht. But they were soon blotted out by the night.

The shots had come from the right. Rainsford doggedly swam in that direction for a seemingly endless time. Then, out of the darkness, came a high, screaming sound of an animal in terror—cut short by the crisp, staccato sound of a pistol shot.

He was almost on the rocks before he saw them. With his remaining strength, he dragged himself from the swirling waters. Gasping, he flung himself down and tumbled into deep sleep.

WHEN he opened his eyes it was late afternoon. He saw no sign of a trail through the jungle above the beach; it was easier to go along the shore. Darkness was blacking out both sea and jungle before Rainsford sighted lights shining from a large house on a high bluff. He climbed up stone steps.

A man in uniform, solidly built and black-bearded to the waist, opened the door, revolver in hand.

"Don't be alarmed," said Rainsford. "I fell off a boat. My name is Sanger Rainsford, of New York City."

A tall, white-haired man in evening clothes appeared and held out his hand. "I am General Zaroff. It is a great pleasure to welcome Mr. Sanger Rainsford, the celebrated hunter. I've read your book about hunting snow leopards in Tibet." He made a sign and the man in uniform put away his pistol.

"Ivan is incredibly strong," remarked the general, "and a bit of a savage. He's a Cossack. So am I.

"But come, we shouldn't be chatting here. You want clothes, food, rest. Follow Ivan if you please, Mr. Rainsford."

"PERHAPS you were surprised," said the general as they sat down to dinner later in a baronial hall, "that I recognized your name. I read all books on hunting. I have one passion in life— the hunt."

"You have some wonderful heads here," said Rainsford, glancing at the walls. "That Cape buffalo is enormous. I've always thought the Cape buffalo is the most dangerous of all big game."

"Not so," the general replied. "Here in my preserve I hunt more dangerous game. Of course, it isn't here naturally. I have to stock the island."

"What have you imported, General? Tigers?"

The general grinned. "No, there's no thrill left in tigers, no real danger. I live for danger, Mr. Rainsford."

"But what game . . . ?"

"I'll tell you. It came to me ultimately that I had to invent a new animal to hunt. I asked myself: What are the attributes of an ideal quarry? And the answer was: It must have courage, cunning, and—above all—it must be able to reason. Fortunately, there is one animal that can reason."

"But you can't mean . . . What you speak of is murder."

"An unpleasant word," said the general. "But I hunt the scum of the earth—sailors from tramp ships. Come to the window." Far out at sea there was a flash of lights as he pressed a button. "The lights indicate a channel where there are only razor-edged rocks. They can crack a ship like a nut.

"It—is a game, you see. I suggest to one of my visitors that we go hunting. I give him three hours' start. I follow, armed only with a .22 pistol. If my quarry eludes me for three whole days, he wins. If I find him"—the general smiled—"he loses."

"Suppose your quarry refuses to be hunted?"

"Then I turn him over to Ivan, a simple fellow who once served as official flogger to the Great White Tsar and has his own ideas of sport. Invariably they choose the hunt."

"And if they win?"

The general's smile widened. "To date I have not lost, although one did almost win. I eventually had to use the dogs. Observe." He led the way to another window. Below, Rainsford could see a dozen or so huge black shapes moving about.

"And now I want to show you my latest collection of heads. Will you come to the library? No? Ah, indeed. You need a good night's sleep. Tomorrow you'll feel like a new man."

GENERAL ZAROFF did not appear the next day until luncheon. Rainsford saw his dead-black eyes studying him. "Tonight," said the general, "we will hunt—you and I."

"No, General," Rainsford said, "I will not hunt."

The general shrugged. "As you wish. But I suggest that my idea of sport is more diverting than Ivan's. You'll find this game worth playing—your brain, your woodcraft, your stamina against mine."

"And if I win . . . ," began Rainsford.

"If I do not find you by midnight of the third day, I'll acknowledge defeat. My sloop will place you on the mainland. I give my word.

"Now," said General Zaroff with a businesslike air, "Ivan will supply you with hunting clothes, food, a knife. I suggest you avoid the big swamp in the southeast corner of the island. We call it Death Swamp. There's quicksand there. I shall not follow until dusk. Hunting at night is much more exciting, don't you think?"

RAINSFORD had fought his way through the bush for two hours, spurred by the sharp rowels of something approaching panic. Now he stopped to take stock.

"I'll give him a trail to follow," he thought, striking off into trackless wilderness. Recalling fox-hunt lore, the dodges of the fox, he executed a series of intricate loops, doubling back again and again on his trail. Darkness found Rainsford, leg-weary, on a thickly wooded ridge. "The fox," he thought, "and now the cat." A big tree with thick, outspread branches was nearby. Taking care to leave no marks, he climbed up and stretched out on one of its broad limbs.

Night crawled slowly by. Toward morning he heard something coming through the bush, slowly, carefully. He flattened himself against the bough and, through a thick screen of leaves, watched.

It was General Zaroff. He made his way along, eyes fixed in concentration on the ground. He paused almost beneath the tree, dropped to his knees and studied the ground. Then, straightening, he lit a long black cigarette.

Rainsford held his breath as the general's eyes traveled inch by inch up the tree. But the sharp eyes of the hunter stopped before they reached the limb where his quarry lay. Very deliberately, Zaroff smiled and blew a smoke ring into the air. Then he walked carelessly away.

The pent-up air burst from Rainsford's lungs. His first thought: Clearly the general could follow a difficult trail through the woods at night; only by chance had he failed to see his quarry.

Then came a second thought: Why had the general smiled? Why had he turned back? The general was playing with him, saving him for another day's sport. Now Rainsford knew the meaning of terror.

Sliding down from the tree, he set off into the woods. Three hundred yards away he stopped where a huge, dead tree leaned precariously on a smaller, living one. He took his knife from its sheath and set to work. When the job was finished, he threw himself down behind a fallen log a hundred feet away. He did not have to wait long.

So intent on the trail was the Cossack that he was upon the thing before he saw it. His foot touched the protruding bough—the trigger. The general sensed danger and leaped back, but not quite quickly enough; the dead tree crashed down and struck him a glancing blow. He stood there, rubbing his injured shoulder, and his mocking laugh rang through the jungle.

"Rainsford," he called, "let me congratulate you. Not many men know how to make a Malay man-catcher. You are proving interesting, Mr. Rainsford. I am going now to have my wound dressed; it is only a slight one. Don't worry, I'll be back."

When the general had gone, Rainsford again took up his flight. Dusk came, then darkness, and the ground grew softer under his moccasins. He stepped forward and his foot sank into ooze. Death Swamp!

The softness of the earth gave him an idea. Stepping back from the quicksand a dozen feet, he began to dig. When the pit was above his shoulders he climbed out and from some hard saplings cut stakes, sharpening them to a fine point. These he planted at the bottom of the pit, points up. He wove a rough carpet of weeds and branches to cover the mouth of the pit. Then, wet with sweat, he crouched behind a tree.

By the padding sound of feet on the soft earth he knew his pursuer was coming. Then he heard breaking branches—and the sharp scream of pain as the stakes found their mark. He looked. Three feet from the pit stood a man with a flashlight.

"Rainsford!" cried the general. "Your Burmese tiger pit has claimed one of my best dogs. Again you score. I must now see what you can do against my whole pack. Thank you for a most amusing evening."

AT DAYBREAK Rainsford, near the swamp, was awakened by a distant sound, faint and wavering—the baying of hounds. For a moment he stood thinking. A native trick he had learned in Uganda came to him.

He headed away from the swamp and quickly found a springy young sapling. To it he fastened his hunting knife, the blade pointing back down the trail. With a bit of wild grapevine he tied back the sapling ... and ran for his life. As the hounds hit the fresh scent, they howled, and Rainsford knew how an animal at bay feels.

The noise of the hounds stopped abruptly. Rainsford's heart stopped, too. They must have reached the knife.

Shinning excitedly up a tree, he looked back. His pursuers

had stopped. But hope died, for he saw that General Zaroff, gun in hand, was still on his feet. The knife, driven by the recoil of the springing tree, had instead caught Ivan who had been holding the dogs in leash.

Hardly had Rainsford got back to the ground when, once more, the pack took up the cry.

"Nerve, nerve!" he panted to himself as he dashed along. A blue gap showed through the trees ahead. He reached the sea, and across a cove could see the gray stone of the large house. Twenty feet below him the sea rumbled and hissed. Rainsford hesitated. Then he leaped far out into the water.

When the general and his pack reached the opening, the Cossack stopped. For some moments he stood regarding the blue-green expanse of water.

AT DINNER that evening two annoyances kept General Zaroff from perfect enjoyment. One, it would be difficult to replace Ivan; the other, that his quarry had escaped him. Of course, the suicidal American had not played the game. To soothe himself the general read in his library. At ten, comfortably tired, he went to his bedroom.

Before turning on the light he went to the window and looked down on the courtyard. He could see the great hounds in the moonlight, and he called, "Better luck another time." Then he switched on the light.

A man who had been hiding in the curtains of the canopied bed was standing before him.

"Rainsford!" screamed the general. "How in God's name did you get here?"

"Swam. I found it quicker than walking through the jungle."

The other sucked in his breath and smiled. "I congratulate you. You have won the game."

Rainsford did not smile. "I am still a beast at bay," he said, in a low, hoarse voice. "Get ready, Zaroff."

The general made one of his deepest bows. "I see," he said. "Splendid. One of us is to furnish a repast for the hounds. The other will sleep in this excellent bed. On guard, Rainsford . . ."

HE HAD NEVER SLEPT in a better bed, Rainsford decided.

Mr. Todd, The Man Who Liked Dickens

by Evelyn Waugh

ALTHOUGH MR. TODD had lived in Amazonas for nearly 60 years, no one except a few families of Pie-wie Indians was aware of his existence. His house stood in a small savanna, a little patch of sand and grass three miles or so across, bounded on all sides by forest. Todd owned a small herd of cattle, a cassava plantation and some banana and mango trees.

One day a Pie-wie came to Mr. Todd with news that a white man, an explorer, was approaching through the forest, alone and very sick.

The man was already clear of the bush when Mr. Todd reached him. He was without hat or boots; his feet were cut and grossly swollen; every exposed surface of skin was scarred by insect and bat bites. He was talking to himself in delirium but stopped when Mr. Todd addressed him.

"I'm tired," the man mumbled. "Can't go any farther."

Supporting him by the arm, Mr. Todd led the man across the hummocks of grass toward his house.

"It is a very short way. When we get there I will give you something to make you better."

"You speak English," the man said. "I'm English, too. Name is Last."

"Well, Mr. Last, you aren't to bother about anything more. I'll take care of you."

Last's recovery was slow. At first, days of lucidity alternated with delirium; then his temperature dropped and he was conscious even when most ill. Mr. Todd dosed him regularly with herbal remedies.

"There is medicine for everything in the forest," explained Mr. Todd. "My mother was an Indian and she taught me many of them."

"But surely you are English?"

"My father was, a Barbadian. He came to Guiana as a missionary. It is not 20 years since he died. He was a man of education. Can you read?"

"Of course."

"Not everyone is so fortunate. I cannot."

Last laughed apologetically. "But I suppose you haven't much opportunity here."

"Oh, I have a *great* many books. I will show you. Until five years ago there was a man here, well educated. He used to read to me every day. You shall read to me when you are better."

"I shall be delighted."

"Yes, you shall read to me," Mr. Todd repeated.

The days passed without distinction. The first time Last left the house Mr. Todd took him for a little stroll.

"I will show you Mr. Washington's grave," he said, leading him to a mound beneath the mango trees. "He was very kind to me. Every afternoon until he died, for two hours, he read to me. I think I will put up a cross—to commemorate his death and your arrival—a pretty idea."

When Last had passed six or seven consecutive days without fever, Mr. Todd said, "Now I think you are well enough to see the books."

At one end of the hut there was a kind of loft formed by a rough platform erected up in the eaves of the roof. Mr. Todd propped a ladder against it and mounted. Last followed, still unsteady after his illness. Mr. Todd sat on the platform and Last stood at the top of the ladder looking over. There was a heap of small bundles there, tied up with rag, palm leaf and rawhide.

"It has been hard to keep out the worms and ants. Two are practically destroyed."

Todd unwrapped the nearest parcel and handed down a calf-bound book. It was an early American edition of *Bleak House*.

"You are fond of Dickens?" asked Last.

"More than fond. You see, they are the only books I have ever heard. My father used to read them, and then later Mr. Washington...and now you. I have heard them all several times by now but I never get tired; there is always more to be noticed, so many characters, so many changes of scene, so many words...I have all Dickens's books except those that the ants devoured. It takes a long time to read them all—more than two years."

"Well," said Last lightly, "they will well last out my visit."

"Oh, I hope not. It is delightful to start again. Each time I think I find more to admire."

That afternoon Last had his first reading. He had always rather enjoyed reading aloud.

The old man sat astride his hammock opposite Last, following the words, soundlessly, with his lips. Often when a new character was introduced he would say, "Repeat the name, I have forgotten him," or, "Yes, yes, I remember her well. She dies, poor woman." He would frequently interrupt with questions about the characters.

At the end of the first day the old man said, "You read beautifully. It is almost as though my father were here again." And always at the end of a session he thanked his guest courteously. "I enjoyed that *very* much. It was an extremely distressing chapter. But, if I remember rightly, it will all turn out well."

One day, running his thumb through the pages of *Bleak House* that remained to be read, Last said, "We still have a lot to get through. I hope I shall be able to finish it before I go, but the time has come when I must be thinking about getting back to civilization. I have already imposed myself on your hospitality for too long."

Mr. Todd made no reply.

"How soon do you think I shall be able to get a boat? I appreciate all your kindness to me more than I can say, but I really must be getting back..."

"My friend, any kindness I may have shown is amply repaid by your reading of Dickens. Do not let us mention the subject again."

"Forgive me, Mr. Todd, but I really must press the point. When can I get a boat?"

"There is no boat."

"Well, the Indians can build one."

"You must wait for the rains. There is not enough water in the river now."

"How long will that be?"

"A month . . . two."

THEY HAD FINISHED *Bleak House* and were nearing the end of *Dombey and Son* when the rain came.

"Now it is time to make preparations to go."

"Oh, that is impossible. The Indians will not make a boat during the rainy season—it is one of their superstitions. Did I not mention it? And now if you have finished your meal, perhaps we might have another chapter?"

Weeks passed. They read *Nicholas Nickleby* and *Little Dorrit* and *Oliver Twist*. One day, nearly a year after Last had left England, a prospector arrived in the savanna, one of that lonely order of men who wander for a lifetime through the forests. Last scribbled his name on a slip of paper and put it into the man's hand. Sometime, this year or the next, the prospector would arrive at a Brazilian village with news of Last. Meanwhile, the Englishman resumed his unvarying routine with quiet confidence and expectation.

One evening, after a long conference with an Indian neighbor, Mr. Todd proposed a celebration. "It is one of the local feast days," he explained.

Accordingly, after supper they joined a party of Indians assembled round the fire in one of the huts at the other side of the savanna. They were singing in a monotonous manner and passing a large calabash of liquid from mouth to mouth. Separate bowls were brought for Last and Mr. Todd.

"You must drink it all without lowering the cup. That is the etiquette."

Last gulped the dark liquid. It had a flavor of honey and brown bread. He leaned back in the hammock feeling unusually contented. Another calabash was offered him and he handed it back empty. He lay full length watching the play of shadows on the thatch as the Pie-wies began to dance. Then he shut his eyes and thought of England and his wife and fell asleep.

He awoke, still in the Indian hut, with the impression that he had outslept his usual hour. He looked for his watch and found to his surprise that it was not on his wrist.

On the way across the savanna he was obliged to stop more than once, shutting his eyes and breathing deeply. "Treacherous drink, that," he reflected. When he reached the house he found Mr. Todd sitting there.

"Ah, my friend, you are late for the reading this afternoon. There is scarcely another half-hour of light. How do you feel?"

"Rotten. That drink doesn't seem to agree with me."

"I will give you something to make you better."

"You haven't seen my watch anywhere? I thought I was wearing it. I say, I've never slept so long."

"Two days."

"Nonsense. I can't have."

"Yes, indeed. It is a long time. It is a pity because you missed our guests."

"Guests?"

"Why, yes. Three Englishmen. They particularly wished to see you. But what could I do? You were so sound asleep. As you could not greet them yourself I gave them a little souvenir, your watch. They wanted something to take home to your wife who is offering a great reward for news of you. They were very pleased with it. And they took some photographs of the little cross I put up to commemorate your coming.

"I do not suppose they will visit us again, our life here is so retired. I do not suppose we shall ever have visitors again. . . . Well, I will get you some medicine to make you feel better. We will not have any Dickens today . . . but tomorrow, and the day after that, and the day after that. Let us read *Little Dorrit* again. There are passages in that book I can never hear without the temptation to weep."

Unnerving News
of Monsters

Is There a
Champlain Monster?

by Brian Vachon

JANET TYLER, a deputy sheriff in Westport, N.Y., was standing on the porch of her home, which faces a protected cove on Lake Champlain, when she saw a dark creature in the water, head projecting three to four feet above the surface. By the time she got to the phone, whatever was frolicking in the cove in October 1975 had vanished.

Luis Velez owns a marina in Port Henry. In the summer of 1973, he saw something moving through the waters of Lake Champlain that he could not identify. He and friends chased the creature by boat, but it disappeared from sight.

Champ is the name given to this real or imagined monster that has been seen bobbing to the surface of the 120-mile-long waterway between New York and Vermont. As described in more than 130 sightings compiled since the early 1600s, Champ is up to 40 feet long, with two catfish-like horns protruding from a horse-shaped head. Its neck, about one foot thick and five feet long, has a fibrous mane. The bulk of its body is elephant gray or rust color and, according to many sighters, Champ has two or three humps that move in coordination as he undulates through the water. And he moves pretty fast for a big guy—up to 15 miles an hour.

Philip Reines, associate professor of communications and mass media at the State University College of Plattsburgh, N.Y., has been studying nautical phenomena for about 20 years and has become fascinated with the monster. "I believe it is a relatively deep-water creature," Reines offers. (Champlain's average depth is 64 feet, but in spots the lake goes down nearly 400 feet.) "The available evidence indicates that it is nocturnal, shy and solitary by nature." This could account for the relatively few recorded sightings of Champ and explain why most have occurred near deep-water areas.

Believers know that their sanity or sobriety gets questioned when they talk about Champ. Says Roy Fleury, a licensed Adirondack Mountains guide from Westport, "Anyone who's seen that monster has been into the wine bottle. I've spent as much time on the lake as any living soul, and never saw the thing."

Jon Anderson, a Vermont fishery biologist, says he lost a good friend over Champ: "I said I didn't believe there was a monster, and my friend, a fisherman who knows the lake well, said he did. We argued, and haven't spoken to each other since."

French explorer Samuel de Champlain, for whom the lake is named, sighted a strange inhabitant that may have been the monster. Indians had told him about a fish they called *chaousarou*, which could reach eight to ten feet in length. In July 1609, Champlain wrote that while on the lake he saw a *chaousarou* "five feet long, as thick as a man's thigh, with silvergray scales that a dagger couldn't pierce and two-and-a-half-foot jaws filled with lethal teeth." Further on, the report said, "The Indians gave me a head of it, which they prize highly, saying when they have a headache, they let blood with the teeth of this fish at the seat of the pain, which immediately goes away."

In 1819, pioneers were flabbergasted when the monster stuck his head above the waters of Bulwagga Bay. So many sightings were reported in the 1870s that a "monster scare" broke out. A group of New Yorkers on a steamboat excursion unexpectedly saw the monster as they neared the Vermont shore. Later, the *Temperance Advocate* of St. Albans, Vt., gave this report: "The What-Is-It of Lake Champlain was again viewed near Barber's Point on Monday last. It was in full view of passengers aboard the steamer *Curlew*. Although viewed through a glass, it could not be made out distinctly. Parties on the New York side claim the water was strongly agitated for

30 or 40 feet from the erected head of the monster when in motion."

And so it went for the next 20 years. During those decades, the Champlain monster became so famous that showman P. T. Barnum offered $50,000 for the serpent's hide.

No one could deliver, but the sightings never ceased. In August 1939, a couple fishing off Rouses Point spotted a monster. This one, in appearance like most of the others but far more aggressive, began jumping through the water toward the boat. The couple steered straight for shore, and eventually the monster disappeared in the lake's murky waters. But not before the couple received what they readily described as the fright of their lives.

Another sighting is described by L. R. Jones: "On Friday evening at 6 p.m. in the year 1947, I was fishing off the northern tip of North Hero Island with two companions. The lake was calm, undisturbed by the slightest ripple. Suddenly, artd without warning, a tremendous splash was heard in the water north of us. Out of the depths reared a huge dark form which moved swiftly in a northwesterly direction. Three segments appeared, clearly discernible above the water's surface, separated one from the other by about five feet of water, the overall length of the creature being about 25 feet. It moved with incredible swiftness—about 15 miles per hour—and disappeared altogether in about two minutes."

"Reports from honest, reliable folks keep coming in over the years, so the riddle goes on," says Leon Dean, a retired English professor from the University of Vermont and an authority on the monster. "A floating log, an unusual reflection of the lake, ducks, otters swimming one after another, a flock of birds upon the water, all these *could* fool people into thinking they have seen the monster."

Of all the known possibilities, the lake sturgeon, the lake's largest known fish, is probably the best, says Dean. "But even *they* do not meet all the conditions reported time after time," he concedes.

What, then, can finally be said about Champ observers? Well, they are not alone. The world is filled with lakes that purportedly provide homes for sea monsters. Most are deep, cold-water lakes in nations that lie between mild, temperate forest belts and frozen tundra belts. There are reports of monsters in scores of lakes: Loch Ness in Scotland, Baikal in Russia, Victoria in Africa, and others in Chile, Sweden, Norway, Australia and Canada. In Ireland they talk about the "direful wurrum" lake creatures, and Icelanders shudder over "Skrimsl," a deep-lake denizen. In British Columbia the monster of Okanagan Lake goes by the name "Ogopogo."

Of all the real and imagined lake creatures, Nessie of Loch Ness is probably the best known. An official scientific classification, "Nessiteras Rhombopteryx," has even been proposed for it.

If a monster can live in Loch Ness, whose waters cover 27.5 square miles, why not in Champlain, with 435 square miles of lake? "There are many similarities between the two lakes," says Connie Pope, who has studied and chronicled monsters for over ten years. "Both lakes were glacially cut, are now landlocked, but were once part of a greater sea. Both still have outlets to the sea, are fresh-water, somewhat remote and fairly unpolluted."

Another thing the two lakes have in common, according to Pope, is that they "never give up their dead." With temperatures around 40 degrees Fahrenheit, bodies can be preserved in Lake Champlain, and water pressures can keep bodies down. This could account for the fact that no monster carcasses have ever been found.

But if creatures do live in Lake Champlain, what are they? Surely not mammal. Mammals have to breathe air, which can't be done beneath a lake when it freezes over. (For all but 12 of the last 150 winters, Lake Champlain has become completely frozen in early February.) It is doubtful that they are reptiles. The temperatures of the lake are much too cold for many reptiles known to modern man.

The theories are legion. Champ *could* be a large eel or sturgeon. He could be one or many. He could be a species unknown to modern biology. But, most important, he could *be*. Anybody for an open mind?

On the Trail
of the Abominable Snowman

by Edward W. Cronin, Jr.

EACH YEAR, stories of the yeti—better known as the Abominable Snowman, a monster man-ape roaming the snows—come rolling down out of the Himalayas like an avalanche. Eyewitness reports, photographs and plaster casts of footprints accumulate into a morass of confusing information.

Why is there so much excitement about the hypothetical existence of the yeti? The interest, in part, has to do with the very confusion and mystery that surround the beast. In an age when science, with heartless efficiency, has solved many enigmas of life, here is one that cannot be readily disposed of. For many people, the yeti is a symbolic stone to hurl at science. "A large man-ape is alive on our crowded planet," the yeti advocate enthuses, "and we can't even find it!"

Interest also has to do with the creature itself, which may be a close relative from our distant and forgotten past. The yeti could be the most significant zoological and anthropological discovery of the century, offering comparative insights into our own development, behavior and prehistoric society.

From 1972 to 1974, I was in the Himalayas as leader of a wildlife expedition, conducting the first ecological survey of the remote Arun Valley in far-eastern Nepal. The Arun is one of the world's deepest river valleys, an isolated haven for wildlife between the towering massifs of Everest and Kanchenjunga, the first and third highest mountains on Earth. Prior to our expedition, the valley had remained relatively unexplored because of the rugged topography, inaccessibility and dense vegetation. Its fauna and flora had never been critically studied.

Numerous reports of the yeti have come from the Himalayas for some 200 years. Villagers relate stories about it that date back many generations, and some claim to have recently seen yeti. The first Westerner to have published an account of the yeti was B. H. Hodgson in 1832. Since then, more than 40 Westerners, including highly reputable individuals, have described sighting the yeti or its footprints.

Eyewitness reports—from the Himalayas, the Soviet Union, and China, which are remarkably consistent—construct a detailed description. Its body is stocky, ape-like in shape. It stands 5½ to 6 feet tall, and is covered with short, coarse hair, reddish-brown to black, sometimes with white patches on the chest. The hair is longest on the shoulders. The face is hairless and rather flat. The jaw is robust; the teeth are quite large, the mouth is wide. The head comes to a pointed crown. The arms are long, reaching almost to the knees. The shoulders are heavy and hunched. There is no tail.

Although the sightings must be taken on faith, photographs of yeti footprints contribute concrete data. The most noteworthy discovery of footprints was made by Eric Shipton and Michael Ward in 1951 but since then, tracks have been photographed by many other travelers. The prints were made on a thin layer of crystalline snow lying on firm ice, indicating that little erosion or melting had occurred. Photographs the men took are exceptionally clear and sharp, showing a foot 12½ inches long by 5 inches wide, with the heel nearly as broad as the forepart. A conspicuous human-like arch is absent. The great toe is quite large, with the second toe the longest and relatively thin, while the remaining three toes are short and stubby. The yeti appears to walk on two rather than four feet.

Any creature existing today must have ancestors, and it may be that the antecedents of the yeti can be found among known fossil ape forms. The size and shape of one fossil form in particular—*Gigantopithecus*—help make it a likely ancestral candidate, for it closely resembles eyewitness descriptions of the yeti. Remains of *Gigantopithecus* have been found in the Himalayan foothills, not far from many modern yeti sightings.

But how could a primate as large as a yeti-*Gigantopithecus* elude its numerous investigators in so relatively small an area for so long? Our findings suggest that such a creature would not inhabit the harsh snowlands, but, like the mountaineers who discover its tracks, may use the snowy passes as routes from one valley to the next. The yeti would favor the middle-altitude zone, where dense forests of oak, magnolia, rhododendron, fir, alder and birch, among others, provide an inible diversity and abundance of plants, and also a hiding place. There are additional aids to concealment: the land's numerous gullies, canyons, cliffs, rock shelters and varied slopes.

Adding to the difficulty of discovery, the yeti is probably nocturnal. Like many other large mammals that suffer from man's disturbance of the wilderness, it has probably developed the habit of hiding and sleeping during the day and traveling and feeding at night.

Thus, the sum total of evidence indicates that there is no zoological, paleontological or ecological reason to suppose that an unknown anthropoid does not exist in the Himalayas. There is, in fact, a significant body of data that warrants a more thorough field investigation.

In December 1972, Dr. Howard Emery, our expedition physician, and I made our first reconnaissance to the high-altitude areas around Kongmaa La mountain to investigate the winter conditions of the ecosystem. On the 17th of the month, accompanied by two Sherpa assistants, we emerged on an alpine ridge. A depression in the ridge at about 12,000 feet offered a flat place with firm snow suitable for camp. The area was small, less than half an acre, a completely clear snowfield unmarked by animal prints.

The slopes on the side of the ridge were precipitous, falling several thousand feet on each side. We pitched two tents, had our dinner around an open fire and retired just after dark. The evening was calm.

Shortly before dawn, Dr. Emery climbed out of our tent and called excitedly. While we were sleeping, a creature had walked directly between our tents. The Sherpas identified the tracks without question as yeti footprints.

We immediately made a full photographic record of the prints before the sun touched them, and later in the day made plaster casts. We devoted special attention to ensure that the prints were not a product of a hoax perpetrated by our Sherpas. Like the conditions Shipton had encountered in 1951, the surface consisted of crystalline snow, excellent for displaying the prints in precise detail. They measured approximately 9 inches long by 4¾ inches wide. The stride, or distance between individual prints, was surprisingly short—often less than one foot—and it appeared that the creature had used a slow, cautious walk. We were impressed with the close resemblance that these prints bore to those found by Shipton.

By the direction of the toes on the footprints, I determined that the creature had come up the north slope. I investigated these prints first, following the trail back down the slope. The snow was very deep, and the tracks consisted of large punch holes, revealing little detail. I descended several hundred yards, but the heavy snow made walking impossible, and I was forced to return to the top of the ridge. The creature must have been exceptionally strong to ascend this slope in these conditions. No human could have made overnight the length of tracks I could see from the top of the ridge.

From our camp, the prints continued onto the south slope, but here the sun had melted most of the snow, and the trail was difficult to follow. We walked farther up the ridge and discovered what appeared to be footprints of the same creature coming back onto the top of the ridge, crossing back and forth several times. The trail then went back down onto the south slope, where we ultimately lost the prints in the bare rock and scrub. During the following 72 hours, we kept day-and-night watch for the reappearance of the creature. But there were no further developments.

Several aspects of this incident provide valuable additional information about the yeti:

1. The circumstances eliminate the hypothesis of some skeptics that all yeti prints are the function of melting by the sun or of wind erosion. We photographed them before sunrise. We knew wind had not affected them, since a comparison of our own footprints made on the morning of the 18th with our footprints made on the 17th showed little, if any, distortion.

2. During the expedition, we made special efforts to examine all large mammal prints found in snow. As professional biologists with extensive experience in the Himalayas, we feel that we can eliminate any possibility that the prints found between the tents were made by any known, normal mammal.

3. The prints support the hypothesis that the various yeti reports refer to one species. The prints are similar to those

photographed by Shipton, differing only in being smaller, perhaps indicating an immature or female yeti.

4. The circumstances support the hypothesis that the yeti
is nocturnal. The creature displayed some inquisitiveness, since
it made a detour along the ridge to enter our camp.

5. The tracks support the hypothesis that the yeti inhabits
the forested regions. They came from a heavily forested valley
and, rather than going in the direction of the higher snowfields,
crossed the ridge and appeared to be continuing back down
toward the forest.

ON THE BASIS of this experience, I believe that there is a creature
alive today in the Himalayas which is creating a valid zoological
mystery. It is possibly a known species in a deformed or abnormal condition, although the evidence points to a new form
of bipedal primate. Or perhaps an old form—a form that man
once knew and competed with, and then forced to seek refuge
in the seclusion of the Himalayas.

Though I am intrigued with the yeti, I would be deeply
saddened to see it captured. We would gain another possession,
another ragged exhibit in the concrete world of the zoological
park, another Latin name to enter on our scientific ledgers. But
what about the wild creature that now roams free in the forests
of the Himalayas? Every time man asserts his mastery over
nature, he gains something in knowledge, but loses something
in spirit.

The Prehistoric Fish
Named L. c. Smith

by James Dugan

On December 22, 1938, at East London, a port in southeast Africa, Miss M. Courtenay-Latimer, the inquisitive curator of the local Museum of Natural History, was examining some sharks brought in by a trawler. Among them she found the body of a surpassing strange fish almost five feet long and weighing 127 pounds. It was steel-blue, with heavy scales, a powerful protruding jaw and padded fins that stuck out like limbs. "It was so peculiar," she said, "that I felt it had to be preserved."

Miss Latimer hauled the "heavy, dirty and oily" fish to the museum and there tried to identify it. She could find nothing like it in her ichthyological references. So she made a sketch and sent it to Professor J. L. B. Smith, the famous fish expert, of Rhodes University College at Grahamstown, South Africa.

Professor Smith, who has discovered and named more than 100 species of fish in his career, looked at this one with something like shock. "My surprise would have been little greater if I had seen a dinosaur walking down the street." For this fish was on the casualty list of animals that died out shortly after the dinosaurs! It was known to scientists only from fragments of fossilized skeletons and from fossil impressions in rocks laid down millions of years ago. Here in front of him was one of the oldest living beings, a creature unchanged in at least 70 million years.

"Though it was difficult to believe so incredible a thing," says Professor Smith, "I identified the fish as a coelacanth (pronounced *see-la-kanth*) and named it *Latimeria* in appreciation of what Miss Latimer had done." Given the species name *chalumnae* (for the Chalumna River, at whose mouth the creature was caught) and the name of the identifier as the usual appendix, the fish became *Latimeria chalumnae* Smith, or *L. c.* Smith.

"Here," said Professor Smith, "is the closest living relative of the long-extinct fish that is accepted as the ancestor of all land animals. He is almost in the direct line of man's ancestry."

The news of *L. c.* Smith made an international sensation. The professor wanted to find other specimens. Thinking that the big rough-hided creature looked like a fish of rocky ledges, he decided that it lived "somewhere about Madagascar." Having no means to organize an expedition, he printed and distributed a descriptive leaflet in English, French and Portuguese, with a photo of the fish, and offering $400 for another coelacanth. World War II blacked out his search, but afterward he and his wife, Margaret, hunted on, tramping the coast, sailing on fishing boats and distributing the leaflets. Years passed without a clue.

In 1952, in Zanzibar, Mrs. Smith gave some leaflets to an English sea captain, Eric Hunt, who ran a trading schooner in the Indian Ocean. A few days before Christmas the Smiths got a cable from Captain Hunt: HAVE COELACANTH IN COMORO ISLANDS. COME AND FETCH IT.

The fish was 2000 miles away; this was the peak of the Southern Hemisphere summer (would the fish decay?); and the professor had no money to charter a plane. He appealed to Prime Minister Daniel F. Malan. The Prime Minister loaned him a military transport plane.

"To my unspeakable relief," says Professor Smith, "the fish turned out to be a true coelacanth."

The fish had been dead nine days, but had been embalmed on the fourth day by Captain Hunt. It had been caught off Anjouan Island in 600 feet of water by a fisherman who had taken it to market. There a schoolteacher recognized it from Smith's leaflet and sent it by bearers 25 miles over mountain trails to Hunt.

As news wires chattered with the story, the administrator of the Comoro Islands received an astringent signal from the Ministry of Overseas Territories in Paris, asking if he had been in siesta while foreigners brazenly flew in and lifted a scientific treasure of France. Whereupon Professor Jacques Millot, then with Paris' Museum of Natural History, entered the big fossil chase and, designated the Scientific Research Institute of Madagascar responsible for all coelacanth taken henceforth in French territory. The Institute duplicated Smith's reward, scattered a ton of reward leaflets and set up fish-embalming stations at strategic ports.

Soon it turned out that the coelacanth had long been well known to the natives: all their lives they had been fishing for it; they had eaten its flesh and used its tough scales to roughen punctured bicycle tubes for patching. Now various kinds of deep-water fish disappeared from the market because the fishermen began baiting for coelacanth alone!

A third coelacanth was taken September 24, 1953, by Houmadi Hassani, a fisherman, off Anjouan Island. Hassani thought he had a shark—the fish fought so vigorously. He maneuvered it to the surface after a half-hour, then, mindful of the authorities' desire to avoid disfiguring the fish, he quelled it with a few thrusts of a *crochet,* or 11-pronged fork. Ashore, he bade his wife guard the big fish well while he ran for Dr. Georges Garrouste, who had one of the Research Institute's embalming kits.

The doctor had been roused many a night by people who said they had captured *le Poisson* but actually had not, so he interrogated Hassani. Hassani said he had a big steel-blue fish with white spots and phosphorescent eyes. Doctor Garrouste had seen Professor Smith's No. 2 fish, a steel-blue monster but which had nothing notable about the eyes except chill and size. He told Hassani to run along. The fisherman persisted. Finally the doctor went with him. He recognized a genuine coelacanth even though it did have white spots and phosphorescent eyes.

The doctor rang the island administrator, M. André Lher. Lher rushed to join the doctor, and the two Frenchmen worked all night injecting formaldehyde into *L. c.* Smith No. 3. They ordered a stout crate built, the airport to hold the mail plane and police to clear the roads for a race to the airport ten miles away.

Professor Millot, waiting in Tananarive, Madagascar, got a virtually undamaged specimen, although the fish had turned brown and the eyes no longer glowed.

Millot handed fisherman Hassani his reward in a public ceremony. The money represents about two years' income for a local fisherman. The coelacanth boom was on. Since Hassani, close to one hundred fishermen have hit the jackpot off the Comoros.

Administrator Georges Savignac of Great Comoro Island was roused at midnight on January 29, 1954, by the arrival of *L. c.* Smith No. 4. "It was very exciting," he said later, "rushing to get it ready. We were finishing up at 4 a.m. when a man staggered in with an even bigger coelacanth. We went to work on it, and loaded the two boxes on the plane. Thirteen days later a third coelacanth was brought in. We were getting tired of fish."

The administrator figured he was in for a busy season, so he ordered a big stock of formaldehyde. No more fish were caught for seven months.

Most the fish taken so far have come from depths ranging from 300 to 1300 feet and were caught at night in a period from September to March. The largest weighed 209 pounds, the smallest 2 pounds. Comoro fishermen say they have caught coelacanth in the past that weighed up to 225 pounds.

To study the anatomy of this unique fish, Millot brought *L.c.* Smith No. 3 back to the Paris museum in January 1954. Over the next seven years, the museum acquired some 20 additional specimens, all captured off the Comoros, and scientists dissected them systematically, sending samples to researchers all over the world.

Early in 1972, an expedition to the Comoro Islands was organized with participants from Britain, the United States and France. It was well timed: during the expedition local fishermen caught two coelacanths. The second fish was still alive when the expedition members reached it, and survived for several hours, enabling them to study a living fish.

Today, more than 40 years after Professor Smith identified the living coelacanth, scientists know a lot about its anatomy. They have found that the heart is a living example of an early stage of heart evolution: the cavities are set out in a line in contrast to the compact organ of more advanced vertebrates. The fins, particularly the side fins—pectoral and ventral—also have an archaic shape and are attached to the body by an articulated peg or peduncle. The brain is small but harmoniously developed.

Scientists believe that the large fatty organ in the abdominal cavity is vestige of a lung, and this sheds new light on the question of how the primitive fish, which was man's ancestor, was able to breathe when it left its water environment to settle on land. The tissue, for the most part, "is remarkable for its ordinariness," said Professor Millot, "any competent medical student could probably identify at first glance in the microscope most of the organs, as the cells are disposed roughly as in our own bodies."

The experts have hardly begun on the colossal riddle of how the fish survived the extinction of all known forms of its period. Coelacanth probably owe their survival at least partly to their great anatomical robustness and their ability to live in great depths. They also found in the Comoros waters adequate salinity and favorable temperature 57 to 64 F. as well as natural protection from predators.

A new chapter in the saga of coelacanth began on January 5, 1972, when the 67th specimen was captured off of an Anjouan island. It was a female, and it contained 19 mature, but unfertilized eggs, each the size of an orange. Each egg weighed ten ounces and was surrounded by a soft membrane. Now researchers turn to the next question: were the eggs fertilized and incubated inside or outside the mother's body?

The answer came three years later when the American Museum of Natural History in New York decided to open its specimen, L. c. Smith No. 26, which had been captured in January 1962. The fish contained five embryos. Each was about one foot in length and had a yolk sac still attached for its nourishment. The embryos appeared to be fully developed and ready to be released. One important riddle was now solved: coelacanth produced eggs which were fertilized and incubated inside the fish's body. Says Professor Jean Anthony, who succeeded Millot: "One can easily imagine that man's true fish ancestor had the same mode of reproduction."

Scientists are now hunting for a pregnant coelacanth with embryos that are less developed than the ones found in L. c. Smith No. 26, for they may provide a miniature history of evolution. During its growth, the embryo changes physically, casting off vestigial characteristics from day to day. The study of a young embryo could thus possibly permit better knowledge of life forms millions of years ago.

"Meanwhile," says Professor Anthony, "L. c. Smith has become very precious to us. Thanks to it, we have been able to determine the biology of coelacanth, a group of fish believed to be extinct 70 million years ago. It has also allowed us to formulate reasonable hypotheses about its distant relative, that lived more than 300 million years ago."

Professor J. L. Smith died in 1968. But his name will always be linked with the capture and identification of the living coelacanth, rightly described as "the most amazing event of the century in the realm of natural history."

Call It a Miracle

Phantom of the Woods

by Doris Cheney Whitehouse

IT WAS LATE when I got off duty. I didn't even stop to change my uniform, but went directly out into the woods which surrounded the neuropsychiatric wing of the big hospital. The leaves under my feet were thick and dry, and as I waded through them I was aware of the tangy smell of autumn. The keys to Ward 8, worn on a long rope about my waist, jingled as I walked—reminding me that I was a part of the outside world, free to come and go at will. At the moment this seemed to be the one indisputable difference between Anthony Di Nardo and me.

Tony was a young soldier, a victim of combat fatigue. Diagnosis: agitated depression, manic-depressive type. I was a nurse, sound of mind, on loan from a civilian hospital. And yet, that very afternoon, standing together on the sun porch of Ward 8, Tony and I had shared an incredible vision. The thing we had seen was somewhere in these woods. I had to find out what it really was, to prove to him that it was only an illusion, and thereby end its threat to his recovery.

I thought about the day that Tony had been admitted, three months before. I saw him as he was then, bound to a canvas litter, his tousled hair ebony-black against the pillow. I had watched as a medical corpsman removed his straps and led him into a naked room where he was to be confined for seven weeks. Beneath gray pajama sleeves, white bandages encircled both his wrists.

His face was angular and elongated, and in it I saw a quality of tenderness. Something within me had stirred with an answering tenderness, so that during the days that followed I favored him over all the others.

Tony had been evacuated from his post in the Pacific, where on a certain morning he had removed the double-edged blade from a razor and slashed the arteries in both his wrists. All through the early days of his stay in Ward 8, the pale hands tore at their restraints in a desperate effort to rip apart the sutures which had robbed him of release. For seven weeks he did not speak or even lift his eyes. There was no violence in him—only the burning desire to be allowed to die. This, through constant vigil, we denied him.

And then, in time, the tortured hands relaxed, and the wounds began to heal. Slowly the spirit found its way out of the darkness. I watched him as he moved about the ward, straight and sure. I saw his healing heart expand to include his fellow patients, and saw him ministering to their needs with the wisdom of one who knew the demons that possessed them.

Tony Di Nardo was almost well. Even our skeptical chief nurse, Barbara Rankin, was forced to concede it. But then, without warning, on this day in late October, a phantom thing had threatened to destroy him.

The day had begun like any other. I reported for duty at 7 a.m. At noon I went to lunch. Rankin was waiting for me in her office when I got back. "You'd better go and have a look at your protégé," she said.

"What's wrong?" I asked.

"Oh, nothing much." Her voice was granite. "He just got a little excited when he saw the Virgin Mary standing in the woods, that's all!"

I turned and ran to Ward 8. I found him kneeling on the floor, his forehead pressed against the wire screening which surrounded the sun porch of the ward. His eyes were fixed on a spot somewhere out in the woods. He was praying softly.

I tried to make my voice sound light, but it came out harsh and shaky. "Whatever are you *doing,* Tony?" I said. "Get up!"

"But you don't understand," Tony said. "I can see the Virgin standing there!" Then he looked up at me, his eyes entreating as though he were struggling with his own reason. "Is there a statue out there?" he asked.

"No, Tony. I know those woods. There's nothing out there. Now, *please,* get up!"

He turned from me and looked out again into the woods. For a long time I stood above him, wishing that I could take the dark head in my hands and soothe away the dreadful danger. But one does not do such a thing, especially when one is a student nurse.

Instead my eyes wandered absently out over the woods, while a dreaded word rose up and pushed against my throat: *hallucination.* Now he must indeed be judged insane.

But as I gazed, my eyes were drawn to something white— and there in the distance among the trees I saw the figure of the Virgin!

I must have cried aloud, because Tony turned his head and looked at me. "Ah, you see her, too!"

"Yes, I see her, too . . ." .

THE REST of the afternoon passed slowly, but at last I was off duty and free to search for the strange Madonna. I felt relief in the knowledge that I had only to find the logical source of the illusion to prove that Tony was not hallucinating.

It was getting dark and cold. I folded my arms against my body underneath my cape, shivering. And then I saw it, just ahead of me.

A white birch stump, tall and slender, carved by the hand of time and weathered into an abstract image of the Madonna. Even at this close range the delicate curve of head and shoulder, the graceful draping of the mantle, were clearly described in the polished stratum of the bark. In those simple lines were all the grace and classic purity ever envisioned by man in his quest for a perfect Madonna.

I rushed back to the ward. Tony was sitting on a wooden bench, staring out into the woods. He spoke without looking up. "Well, did you find what you were looking for?"

Suddenly I was afraid. Tony had pulled himself together and now seemed prepared for a simple answer, logical and conclusive. But I knew that I had stumbled upon something inscrutable, a thing which transcended all logic and all reason. Yet I was afraid that Tony was not well enough to cope with such a mystery. Therefore, I closed my heart against the beauty I had found and whispered, "It was nothing—just a white birch stump. You mustn't think about it any more."

I SHOULD have known that it would not end there.

Late in November, Tony was transferred to an open ward where he was free to come and go about the hospital grounds. Seeing him grow stronger day by day, I began to believe that I had been wise in keeping silent about what I had really seen. So I held the lovely secret in my heart, hoarding it—and I suppose there was talk among my friends about how often I walked alone in the barren woods.

It was a week before Christmas. My training period was over. I said good-by to Tony, and learned that he had been given leave to go home for the holidays. Then I went to my room and began to pack. Suddenly I saw that a light snow was falling, just beginning to adhere to the branches of the trees. On an impulse I got my coat and went outside.

The wind was cold on my face and I blinked my eyes against it. My heart was beating very fast and I began to run. And then, within a few yards of my destination, I stopped.

There, on a glistening blanket of snow, clad in a heavy coat of olive drab, a solitary figure knelt, the white flakes falling like weightless feathers on his bare head. He knelt at the feet of the woodland Madonna, which was clothed in a new white-ness, and the falling snow surrounded and enveloped them both.

When he finished his prayer, I did a thing that one does not do when one is a student nurse. I moved to the place where he knelt and stood behind him, taking the dark head in my hands. Lightly I brushed away the snow that had collected in his hair. "You'll catch your death of cold," I said.

He looked up at me and I could see that he had been expecting me.

"Miracles come in many sizes," he said.

Then he stood and turned to face me, smiling. And in his smile were all wisdom and all tenderness—and I knew that he was well.

The Two-Edged Dagger
of Yusof Hussein

by D. R. Halford-Watkins, M.C.

I VERY NEARLY shot dead a small Malayan police corporal, Yusof Hussein bin Jaffa, two days after I met him. No one would have blamed me; it would have been considered self-defense. But if I had killed him, I wonder—would I be alive today?

It happened in 1948. I was a British officer stationed in Singapore when, early that year, full-scale Communist guerrilla war broke out in Malaya almost overnight, largely carried out by Chinese Communists. From Malaya, a peninsula smaller than the state of Florida, comes one third of the world's tin and nearly half the world's rubber. This was one of the Chinese targets.

A veteran of southeast-Asian jungle campaigns, I was ordered north at once to take over the Rengam police district in the turbulent state of Johore. Our task would not be easy. The 1500 square miles of treacherous jungle and swamp where my 1200 Malay and white troops were supposed to keep law and order was reputedly one of the worst terrorized areas in the country. Political murders were averaging two a day. Arson, torture, robbery, extortion, kidnapings and ambushes were commonplace. The terrorists could raid, plunder and kill, melt back into the jungle and bury their weapons, then walk out as innocent-seeming as the next peaceable rubber tapper. The

Communists hoped by August to declare Malaya a "people's republic" affiliated with Red China.

That was the dark outlook when Haji, the grizzled Malay sergeant major, welcomed me at Rengam police headquarters and introduced me to the noncommissioned officers of my jungle squads. The leader of the crack squad, with the highest number of Communist "kills," was Corporal Yusof Hussein.

I had heard of his exploits even in Singapore. He was an established hero among his fellow Malays—with a reputation further enhanced by the fact that he was the proud possessor of a *Kain Merah,* a rare award made by a *mulvi* (Moslem priest) to a select few of the outstandingly faithful. Literally meaning "red cloth," the *Kain Merah* consists of tiny scrolls of Mohammedan religious scripts encased in red cloth and twisted into a cord-type amulet worn around the upper left arm. Malays, devout Moslems all, believe that it renders the wearer invulnerable to death from knife or gunshot wounds, and by all accounts Yusof's *Kain Merah* had taken him through many daring actions unharmed.

Frankly, I put little stock in his religious trinket. But be that as it may, Yusof Hussein startled me rather unpleasantly when Haji first introduced him. A handsome 29-year-old, with close-cropped black hair and a flashing smile, he had a jaunty air strikingly different from the proud but always quietly polite manner of most Malays. Too cocky; perhaps that was what put me off. I gave him the Malay greeting *"Ada baik?"*—"Are you well?"—and he replied with a grin: "No, Tuan, I am not on a bike; I am walking."

It was a far-fetched pun, an attempt to air his sketchy knowledge of English. I was annoyed. Here, I thought, is a man who bears watching. Two days later, on our first patrol, Yusof Hussein did indeed reveal his true colors.

I had set off in a jeep with Yusof and five constables from his jungle squad to inspect an outpost camp on an isolated rubber estate some 15 miles away. As we rounded a sharp downhill bend a volley of small-arms fire from the green cliff of foliage on our right cracked the jeep's cylinder block. By zigzagging the disabled vehicle violently downhill we managed to get past the ambush party's immediate "killing zone," then flung ourselves into cover by the roadside. As the shooting died down, one could hear the calls of signaling Chinese. It was plain that two parties were closing in and that we were badly outnumbered.

Suddenly, from the far side of a small clearing a voice shouted in Malay with a strong Chinese accent: *"Oi! Orang melayu!*—Hey, you Malays! Give us the white man. Throw out your arms and be safe—we want only the white man!"

Again aching silence. And then—

"Oi! Baik lah!" It was Yusof Hussein's voice ringing out. "Okay. I surrender. Here is my gun." A carbine flashed out into the dappled sunlight of the clearing.

With the much-admired Corporal Yusof selling me out, I knew that I could hardly count on the support of the other constables. I shifted my weapon to bear on the probable location of Yusof Hussein and waited, my finger on the trigger, concealing my position until I could be certain of his. Then a movement on the far edge of the clearing distracted me; three terrorists were crawling forward to retrieve the gun. They had almost reached it when Yusof yelled: *"Oi!—ini juga"*—"Take this too!"

In deeply frightening moments, little things can stand out excruciatingly clear. I can still hear the ear-clapping explosion, still see the dirt-streaked black-red flash, as Yusof's hand grenade burst on the three Communists. And I can still feel the shower of dirt and stones that pelted down on me as a sort of reproach for my false judgment of Yusof Hussein.

While the smoke hovered in a flat blue wraith over the dead, Yusof darted forward to recover his weapon, and all hell broke loose. I yelled: *"Yusof—sini!*—over here!"

He ran back, dodging and weaving, and plunged into the ferns beside me. He flashed a wide grin from ear to ear. "Tuan, sorry if I gave you a bad moment there." He thought it was funny.

Together we managed to assemble our men and gain higher ground, leaving the two enemy parties to bash away at empty bush. Corporal Yusof walked next to me for a time, a mischievous glint in his eye.

"That was a clever ruse, Corporal," I told him. "I don't mind admitting you had me worried for a while. But the main thing is that we got out alive."

"Yah, Tuan," he assented, and his face lost its impish smile as his fingers reverently touched the Red Cloth on his left arm.

As we continued our endless game of hide-and-seek with the jungle Communists, I came really to know and to place complete trust in Corporal Yusof Hussein. He was loyal, courageous, resourceful, and if I admired his bravery I respected his piety too. He prayed at dawn and dusk as a good Moslem does—in the barracks, or during our long jungle patrols—facing Mecca, kneeling, hands on knees, and sometimes prostrating himself. And I came also to value his *Kain Merah* as an emblem of his faith and valor which was helpful to him and his men in battle.

The Red Cloth got an impressive test late that summer when, just a half mile out of Rengam, we saw too late a felled tree blocking the road. Our jeep overturned, spilling us out, and we rushed past the guerrillas' fire lines and assembled a hundred yards up the road. There I missed Yusof, and saw him lying motionless in the road beside the overturned jeep.

Yelling to our chaps to open fire and cover me, I ran back and managed to drag Yusof to the safety of the roadside ditch. He was unconscious, with a large but shallow wound in the back of his head where the jeep had clipped him as it upset. Other troops arrived from Rengam then, and the situation was well in hand when one of the lads said, "Tuan, look—your back is bleeding." I had taken a bullet under the left shoulder blade. Luckily it hadn't gone into the lung, but it put me in hospital for nearly two weeks.

Meanwhile Yusof, on leave, took his patched head to his native village. Near the end of my hospital stay he presented himself at the door of my room, resplendent in his "day off" clothes—a long, silver-and-blue silk *sarong* and a loose-fitting *baju* (jacket) of orange silk with two roomy pockets. He seemed strangely ill at ease as he stood there and tried, unsuccessfully, to smile. "Tuan," he said shyly, "may I come in?"

I motioned him to a chair. But he refused to sit down, and stood shifting awkwardly from foot to foot. Finally he blurted out: "Tuan, I am very grateful to you that you saved my life."

"Nonsense, Corporal, that was just how the breaks were," I replied. "You'd do the same for me."

Yusof persisted. "Tuan," he repeated, "you saved my life." He dug his hand into the pocket of his *baju* and brought out a little six-inch cylinder of wood, beautifully grained and polished. "I would be honored if you would accept this small *kris*—a token of my gratitude."

Opening the cylinder, he showed me a perfectly contrived

miniature of the famous Malay short-sword, the dreadful dagger (now outlawed) with a wavy-edged blade. At the hilt end of the murderous blade is a slender tang that fits into the precious handle: when a *kris* is thrust into an enemy a deft twist of the handle can snap the tang and leave the blade inside the victim.

"Few people can make a good *kris* today," Yusof said. "I had a very old craftsman make this for you." He said he'd also persuaded the village *mulvi* to bless it, and I felt then that I understood his mingled feelings in giving it to me. For he seemed eager for me to have the tiny dagger, yet reluctant to let it go.

"Keep it with you always, Tuan," he said solemnly. "It will bring you luck."

Once I had thanked him and we had spent a few minutes in small talk, he seemed his old self again. "How are you anyway, Tuan?" he asked with the old gleam. *"Ada baik?"*

"Dammit, I'm not on a bike, but I'll soon be walking," I promised. He laughed delightedly at the old joke, then saluted smartly and left.

At the first gray light one morning near the end of 1948, I awoke in my bungalow at Rengam. My phone was ringing. It was the Malay corporal on duty who reported that he'd heard firing. Also, someone had phoned that they'd heard shooting from the direction of the Sembrong estate. He'd tried to ring the estate, but the line was out of order.

I knew Sandy Grant, manager of the estate, his blond wife and their two-year-old daughter. I nipped into my clothes and tore down the gravel path to the waiting vehicles. I always had a stand-by squad on duty, ready to go, and this time it happened to be Yusof Hussein's. I jumped into the lead jeep. Yusof, who always rode directly behind me, tapped my shoulder. "You have the *kris*, Tuan?"

I slapped my canvas cartridge pouch. "Always," I said. *"Baik!"*

We turned into the two-mile-long estate road. It was a rash thing to do. We should have halted and deployed, but with a woman and child under attack we took the gamble. As we approached the estate's office building, machine guns opened up from the second-story windows. We hit the ditch. Oily black smoke billowing from storage sheds on the left told of burning bales of rubber. The Grants' bungalow lay 200 yards beyond.

"We've got to silence those guns—"

Before I finished the sentence Yusof was off across the open ground, grenade in hand. He lunged at the office door and as it flew open a machine gun crackled. Yusof collapsed on the doorstep. His brother, Abdul Rhaman, racing behind him, picked up the grenade and lobbed it home. Then Yusof crawled to the corner of the building and, with Abdul, began sniping at the terrorists who were running from the rear.

Suddenly a frenzied burst of firing broke out to my left. Some terrorists there were attempting a counterattack, and as I looked one of them dashed across the road from the bungalow. If he made it, he would outflank our party in the ditch. Almost without realizing it, I felt my carbine jerk three times. The bullets sent the terrorist spinning.

Bullets continued to fly until finally the counter-attack was broken. I raced for the Grants' bungalow, where I found Sandy Grant and his family barricaded in the bathroom. The mother, fearful that the little girl's cries might attract attention, had plumped her in the half-filled tub where she was splashing happily, unaware of danger.

Then troops arriving from Rengam deployed in the groves; a distant bugle call announced the retreat of the Communists. We could count our losses. Besides Abdul, who was waiting silently by his fallen brother, only one other Malay was left out of the 15 men in Yusof's squad. The Corporal lay, still in the firing position, with his head slumped over his carbine. As I took the weapon from his hands I was torn with emotion. That I had escaped with my own life seemed an incredible miracle.

At Rengam, Sergeant Major Haji greeted me impassively. I slumped into a chair and sketched out the morning's action. "It was unfortunate that the Red Cloth did not work this time for Yusof Hussein," I finished sadly.

"That was hardly surprising, Tuan," he said, and there was new gentleness in old Haji's rumbling voice "—seeing that *you* were carrying it."

I looked up in astonishment. "What the devil do you mean?"

"The *kris* Yusof gave you, Tuan," Haji said imperturbably. "Have you never opened it? The Red Cloth is in the handle of the knife."

Bewildered, I took out the little *kris* and found that the handle slipped easily from the tang. Inside, tightly wrapped, was the *Kain Merah* of Yusof Hussein bin Jaffa. I stared, almost unbelieving, while the *Kain Merah* in my hands became a crimson blur and the full significance of Yusof's act dawned upon me.

I was a Christian who did not believe in his *Kain Merah*, but Yusof Hussein was a Moslem who did. And greater love has no man, whether of his religion or mine, than to lay down his life for a friend.

Miracles?

by Richard Selzer, M.D.

I. JOE RIKER

WHAT IS TO one man a coincidence is to another a miracle. It was one or the other of these that I saw in the spring of 1975. While the rest of nature was in flux, Joe Riker remained obstinate through the change of the seasons. "No operation," said Joe. "I don't want no operation."

Joe Riker is a short-order cook in a diner where I sometimes drink coffee. Every Thursday for six months he had paid a visit to my office. Arriving at four o'clock, he would sit on my examining table, lift the fedora from his head, and bend forward to show me the hole. Gouged from the tonsured top of his head was a mucky puddle, as big as his mouth, whose meaty heaped edge rose above the normal scalp about it. There was no mistaking the announcement from this rampart.

The cancer had chewed through Joe's scalp, munched his skull, then opened the membranes underneath—the dura mater, the pia mater, the arachnoid—until it had laid bare this short-order cook's brain, pink and gray, and pulsating so that with each beat a little pool of cerebral fluid quivered.

I would gaze then upon Joe Riker and marvel. How dignified he was, as though that tumor, gnawing him, denuding his very brain, had given him a grace that a lifetime of good health had not bestowed.

"Joe," I say, "let's get rid of it. Cut out the bad part, put in a metal plate, and you're cured." And I wait.

"No operation," says Joe. I try again.

"What do you mean, 'No operation'? You're going to get meningitis. Any day now. And die. That thing is going to get to your brain."

"No operation," says Joe.

"You give me a headache," I say. And we smile, not because the joke is funny anymore, but because we've got something between us, like a secret.

"Same time next week?" Joe asks. I wash out the wound with peroxide, and apply a dressing. He lowers the fedora over it.

"Yes," I say. "Same time."

But there came a week when Joe Riker did not show up. Nor did he show up for a whole month.

I drive over to his diner. He is behind the counter, shuffling back and forth between the grill and the sink. He is wearing the fedora. He sets a cup of coffee in front of me.

"I want to see you," I say. I am all business.

"Not here," says Joe.

"My office at four o'clock," I say.

"Yeah," says Joe, and turns away.

He is late. Everyone else has gone for the day. Joe is beginning to make me angry. At last he arrives.

"Take off your hat," I say—and he knows by my voice that I am not happy. He raises his fedora straight up with both hands the way he always does, and I see . . . that the wound has healed. Where once there had been a bitten-out excavation, moist and shaggy, there is now a fragile bridge of shiny new skin.

"What happened?" I manage to ask.

"You mean that?" He points to the top of his head. "Oh, well," he says, "the wife's sister, she went to France and brought me a bottle of water from Lourdes. I've been washing it out with that for a month."

"Holy water?" I say.

"Yeah," says Joe. "Holy water."

I see Joe now and then at the diner. He has taken on a terrible ordinariness—a certain dishevelment of the tissues. Did the disease ennoble him, and now that it is gone, is he somehow diminished? Perhaps I am wrong. Perhaps the only change is just the sly wink with which he greets me, as though to signal that we have shared something furtive.

II. YESHI DHONDEN

ON THE BULLETIN BOARD in the front hall of the hospital where I work, there appeared an announcement. "Yeshi Dhonden," it read, "will make rounds at six o'clock on the morning of June 10." The particulars of the meeting were then given, followed by a notation: "Yeshi Dhonden is Personal Physician to the Dalai Lama."

I am not so leathery a skeptic that I would knowingly ignore an emissary from the gods. Thus, on the morning of June 10, I join the clutch of whitecoats waiting in the small conference room adjacent to the ward selected for the rounds. The air in the room is heavy with ill-concealed suspicion. At precisely six o'clock, he materializes, a short, golden, barrelly man dressed in a sleeveless robe of saffron and maroon. His scalp is shaven, and the only visible hair is a scanty black line above each hooded eye.

He bows in greeting while his young interpreter makes the introduction. Yeshi Dhonden, we are told, will examine a patient selected by a member of the staff. The diagnosis is as unknown to Yeshi Dhonden as it is to us. The examination of the patient will take place in our presence, after which we will reconvene in the conference room where Yeshi Dhonden will discuss the case.

The patient had been awakened early, told that she was to be examined by a foreign doctor, and requested to produce a fresh specimen of urine. So, when we enter her room, the woman shows no surprise. She has long ago taken on that mixture of compliance and resignation that is the expression of chronic illness. This was to be but another in an endless series of tests and examinations.

Yeshi Dhonden steps to the bedside while the rest of us stand apart, watching. For a long time he gazes at the woman, favoring no part of her body with his eyes, but seeming to fix his glance at a place just above her supine form. I, too, study her. No physical sign or obvious symptom gives a clue to the nature of her disease.

At last he takes her hand, raising it in both of his own. Now he bends over the bed in a kind of crouching stance, his head drawn down into the collar of his robe. His eyes are closed as he feels for her pulse. In a moment he has found the spot, and for the next half-hour he remains thus, suspended above the patient like some exotic golden bird with folded wings, holding the pulse of the woman beneath his fingers, cradling her hand in his. All the power of the man seems to have been drawn down into this one purpose.

From the foot of the bed, where I stand, it is as though he and the patient have entered a special place of isolation, of apartness, about which a vacancy hovers, and across which no violation is possible. From time to time, the woman raises her head to look at the strange figure above her, then sinks back.

All at once I am envious—not of him, not of Yeshi Dhonden for his gift of beauty and holiness, but of her. I want to be held like that, touched so, *received*. And I know that I, who have palpated a hundred thousand pulses, have not truly felt a single one.

At last, Yeshi Dhonden straightens, gently places the woman's hand upon the bed, and steps back. The interpreter produces a small wooden bowl and two sticks. Yeshi Dhonden pours a portion of the urine specimen into the bowl, and proceeds to whip the liquid with the two sticks. Then, bowing above the bowl, he inhales the odor three times. He sets down the bowl and turns to leave. All this while, he has not uttered a single word. As he nears the door, the woman raises her head and calls out to him in a voice at once urgent and serene. "Thank you, doctor," she says, and touches with her other hand the place he had held on her wrist. Yeshi Dhonden turns to gaze at her, then steps into the corridor. Rounds are at an end.

We are seated now in the conference room. Yeshi Dhonden speaks for the first time, in soft Tibetan sounds that I have never heard before. He has barely begun when the young interpreter starts to translate, the two voices continuing in tandem—a bilingual fugue, one chasing the other. He speaks of winds coursing through the body of the woman, currents that break against barriers, eddying. These vortices are in her blood, he says. Between the chambers of her heart, long, long before she was born, a wind had come and blown open a deep gate that must never be opened. Through it charge the full waters of her river, as the mountain stream cascades in the springtime, battering, knocking loose the land, and flooding her breath. Thus he speaks, and is silent.

"May we now have the diagnosis?" a professor asks.

The host of these rounds, the only man among us who knows, answers.

"Congenital heart disease," he says. "Interventricular septal defect, with resultant heart failure."

A gateway in the heart, I think. That must not be opened. Through it charge the full waters that flood her breath. So! Here then is the doctor listening to the sounds of the body to which the rest of us are deaf. He is more than doctor. He is priest.

NOW AND THEN it happens, as I make my own rounds, that I hear the sounds of his voice, like an ancient Buddhist prayer, its meaning long since forgotten, only the music remaining. Then a jubilation possesses me, and I feel myself touched by something divine.

My Precious Gift
From Conan Doyle

by Selwyn James

TO THE world, Sir Arthur Conan Doyle was the creator of Sherlock Holmes, master detective and brilliant logician. To me, when I was seven, he was the gentle-hearted man who led me through his garden one summer twilight and taught me to believe in the impossible.

The year was 1928. I was already a veteran non-believer in Santa Claus, and suspicious of the well-meant nonsense adults use to ingratiate themselves with children. Yet nothing is so finely etched on my memory as the precious understanding Sir Arthur gave me that evening as we sat waiting among the rhododendron bushes.

Our home was a mile from his big Tudor mansion near the village of Crowborough, England, where he wrote many of the masterfully woven tales that made Holmes and his bumbling friend, Dr. Watson, the best-known sleuths in all fiction. My elder brother, a playmate of the Conan Doyle youngsters, often told of having seen him through his study window writing endlessly on large white sheets of lined paper, his lunch untouched on a tray beside him. "The Great Man Himself," my brother irreverently called him.

One summer afternoon, scrubbed and gleaming in my white flannel suit, I tagged along as my brother's unwanted charge to the Conan Doyle home. While he and the boys played tennis, I wandered off to explore the great rambling house.

Ducking the servants in the corridors, I came at last to a room filled with a dazzling array of painted toy soldiers set up in battle formation on an immense model landscape. A dozen British regiments with tanks, horse-drawn field guns and howitzers were deployed in Flanders fields, while behind the lines were massed reserves ready to join the battle. I stood awe-struck, my heart beating in excitement at the heroic scene.

How long The Great Man Himself had been standing in silence behind me, I do not know. To me he loomed large, a thickset, big-fisted man, forbidding behind his ample Victorian mustache and gold-rimmed spectacles. He wore a heavy, dark suit with high-cut vest and big-knotted tie that seemed far too hot for summertime.

I lost my childish fear of him the moment he started to talk. He did not try to discover my identity with the questions usually asked of unknown children. He seemed to accept my presence in the house quite naturally.

He squatted beside me and pointed out the famous regiments, recounting their battles in words so stirring that my imagination went wild with the sound of gunfire and bomb as the Coldstream Guards made their valiant stand at the Somme. I strode back and forth before them shouting commands, calling for every ounce of their courage, ordering repeated attacks until the enemy fled in confusion.

Then, suddenly, as the first pink-washed rays of sunset slanted through the window, Sir Arthur firmly took my hand. "You're tiring them out," he said—not meaning a reproach, but in the spirit of my game. "They have to fight again to-morrow." As reasonably as if he were announcing supper, he added, "Come on, let's go into the garden and see if we can find the fairies."

I remember glancing at him sharply, disappointed that he was, after all, like other grownups. But not a flicker of mischief was in his face. We went outside—the innocent adult leading the worldly-wise child—and walked across the great lawn to a stone bench surrounded by rhododendron bushes. There we waited, out of sight of the house, until twilight settled over the garden.

"We must sit quite still," Sir Arthur whispered, "or they won't come out."

"Do they *mind* if we see them?" I asked, thinking to humor him.

Sir Arthur must have sensed my skepticism. Patiently he whispered that fairies and pixies will not show themselves to mortals who lack faith in their existence. To see, he said, you must fervently *believe*.

The garden was hushed; it was that hovering instant when time seems to pause and take a breath before plunging into night. I don't remember precisely when it was that I believed. Perhaps when a firefly lit up the tip of my nose, or when a bird or bat fluttered past my head. Maybe it was the pressure of Sir Arthur's huge hand around mine that brought on the wondrous feeling of belief.

I soared with him into a magical world where fantasy is real, where anything is possible. It was a world from which a part of me never came back. Yes, I saw the pixies and fairies as plainly as anything I had seen before or have seen since. A childish hallucination? Perhaps. But with my kindly teacher at my side, I discovered the limitless quality of the human imagination.

For what is true imagination but a belief in the impossible— and what is that but a launching site for creativity? Somerset Maugham saw it this way: "Man consists of body, mind and imagination. His body is faulty, his mind untrustworthy, but his imagination has made him remarkable."

The world Sir Arthur showed me, I am convinced, was visited by the great composers, poets and painters who return to us with their uniquely beautiful patterns of sound and sight. Surely Leonardo da Vinci visited that world, for he saw the vision of man flying like a bird in the sky. It must have been visited, too, by the "impractical" theorists of science who knew the moon was within our grasp centuries before its conquest became a matter of exotic fuels and heat-resistant alloys; by the great men of medicine who, even in the midst of plague, believed that one day mankind would be free of disease; by the ancient dam builders of arid lands who dreamed that deserts could be turned into vineyards—by all the great inventors and creators of every age.

For Sir Arthur Conan Doyle, a belief in the supernatural was perhaps a welcome vacation from the icy logic of the imperturbable Sherlock Holmes—or maybe this belief was actually the wellspring from which his stories flowed.

Is this wonderful world of the imagination the private pre- serve of children and geniuses? It need not be. But many of us are so burdened by the mechanics of plain living that we never pause to hear angels singing to a Brahms symphony or see cherubs sliding down a rainbow.

"It does us good to retreat from common sense," a nuclear physicist once told me. "Now and then we should allow what we *feel* to make a mockery out of what we *know*." Anatole France was even more emphatic: "To know is nothing at all; to imagine is everything."

A brilliant lawyer showed me the "tortured abstracts" he paints for relaxation. "They're what I see in my secret world," he told me. "I wouldn't dare show them to my clients—they would think I was mad."

For others the retreat from common sense may take a different route. A businessman I know hikes off alone deep into the Maine woods for a week every summer. He neither hunts nor fishes. He arms himself only with knapsack and pup tent. "What on earth do you find to do there?" his associates ask him.

To me he confessed. "I eat and drink with the Seven Dwarfs. I walk hand in hand with Hansel and Gretel. And I come out of that wonderful place feeling ten years younger and strong enough in spirit to accomplish anything."

On that summer evening long ago, only my mother was impressed when I told of my adventure with Sir Arthur. "How lucky you are!" she cried. "Haven't I always told you that *nothing* is impossible?" For her, this belief held an exquisite kind of logic that never failed her. Our garden, for instance, was a riot of wildflowers. Mother dug them up in the woods and transplanted them—despite the warnings of horticulturists that they would wither.

"Bring back a palm sapling," she once wrote to my father in Africa. Dutifully, he lugged it home. "It will die—it stands to reason," he predicted glumly. Mother planted it anyway—probably the only palm tree to flourish in an English garden.

That same summer, her belief in the impossible was put to its sternest test. My brother's front tooth was knocked out of its socket by a cricket ball. Though he came home bloody and miserable, Mother had no time for his tears. "Where is the tooth?" she inquired calmly. When my brother shrugged, she whisked us all off to the cricket field where we searched until we found it, miraculously whole, in the grass.

Then we rushed with it to the family dentist. "Put it back!" Mother demanded.

The startled man tried to protest, but he must have seen my mother's eyes burning bright beyond common sense. He stuck the tooth back in my brother's mouth, braced it to the ones on either side, and stitched the gum. Within months the brace was removed. Defying all dental logic, the tooth stayed rooted for the next 28 years. "See what happens when you *believe*," Mother used to say tirelessly.

This same kind of unshakable belief sustained me when my brother and I, separated by World War II, were lost to each other for ten years afterward. Every inquiry I made of such practical sources as British army records, civil service rolls and professional directories failed.

Then one day in 1955 a letter postmarked Southampton, England, came for me in care of the *Reader's Digest*. My brother's wife had by chance seen my by-line on an article in that magazine. Wrote my brother, "I always knew I would find you. As Mother would have said, 'See what happens when you *believe*.' "

Do I still believe in fairies and pixies? I'll say this much: I strongly believe in believing in them. Anything that stimulates the highest reaches of our imagination makes life more joyful—and often more productive. I cherish the world Sir Arthur Conan Doyle introduced to me that summer evening long ago. My own children discovered its wonder, too. Several years ago I came upon Deborah, 6, and Leslie, 17, rapturously watching Mary Martin in a telecast of *Peter Pan*. I looked at my elder daughter closely when Miss Martin announces that Tinker Bell is dying and implores everyone to save her. "If you believe in fairies," she cries, "clap your hands!"

Leslie's eyes were moist as both youngsters clapped vigorously. They turned to me for further support. Then I too began to clap, diverting their attention from my own brimming eyes.

MS READ-a-thon—
a simple way to start youngsters reading

Boys and girls between 6 and 14 can join the MS READ-a-thon and help find a cure for Multiple Sclerosis by reading books. And they get two rewards — the enjoyment of reading, and the great feeling that comes from helping others.

Parents and educators: For complete information call your local MS chapter. Or mail the coupon below.

Kids can help, too!

- -

Mail to:
National Multiple Sclerosis Society
205 East 42nd Street
New York, N.Y. 10017

I would like more information about the MS READ-a-thon and how it can work in my area.

Name_____
(please print)

Address_____

City_____ State_____ Zip_____

Organization_____

78